My Times With
COE

Free Enterprise
At Its Finest

MY TIMES WITH COE

FREE ENTERPRISE
AT ITS FINEST

Fred W. Fields

THE
DONNELL
GROUP

Montgomery, Alabama

The Donnell Group
3514 Lansdowne Drive
Montgomery, AL 36111
334-288-6907
www.thedonnellgroup.com

Printing: Pollock Printing, Nashville, Tenn.

Library of Congress Control Number: 2009940042
ISBN 978-0-965-3313-7-1

First Edition

10 9 8 7 6 5 4 3 2 1

*Dedicated to the
Wood Products Industry*

CONTENTS

PUBLISHER'S NOTE

I have known Fred W. Fields since 1984, which was my first year as a writer for Hatton-Brown Publishers, Inc., a publisher of national and international business magazines that cover the forest products industry. By then, Fields and his company, Coe Manufacturing, was well established as the leading manufacturer of machinery for the softwood plywood industry, and was making great strides with machinery and technologies for the composite panel industry and the softwood lumber industry. When I met Fields, he and Coe were buying up other machinery companies on a regular basis.

Also by 1984, Fields had gained the reputation as a formidable taskmaster. Some of his employees tread softly around him, as I observed at numerous machinery trade shows. This was not a decentralized organization. But I am not sure if these employees understood at the time how much Fields cared for them and protected them.

I liked Fields from the outset. He seemed to like me. Through the years, right up until he sold Coe in 2000, we communicated regularly over the phone, and always sat down for a spell during the trade shows in Portland, Oregon or New Orleans. The talk wasn't all about the wood products industry. We shared a major fondness for sports.

I conducted several lengthy face-to-face interviews with Fields for articles in our magazines. The company always had something going on that was newsworthy, but I was more interested in Fields himself, the make-up of the man. He never revealed too much about his personal life or upbringing, but through the years I picked up bits and pieces of it, enough to want to learn more.

When Fields retired from this industry, nearly ten years ago now, I felt a great loss. Here was a man who epitomized the American Dream, starting out on the family farm during the Great Depression and ultimately purchasing a long-established American manufacturing company and substantially enlarging it.

There are lots of men in many industries like Fred W. Fields. The sad thing is, they go away and the stories of their wonderful lives go with them. Yet the ingenuity and passion that these men demonstrated is a valuable lesson in the business of America.

A couple of years ago I approached Fields about doing this book. He kind of shrugged it off, but I could see in his eyes that I had struck a chord. The result is the book in your hands, a small but defining piece of Americana.

—Rich Donnell

CHAPTER ONE

ALEXANDRIA, INDIANA

Long before my association with it, The Coe Manufacturing Company was a great company and a leading manufacturer of machinery that was applied to the production of veneer, plywood and gypsum board products. There is some tendency on the part of people to think I made Coe into a great company. I would rather say that I did all I could to maintain Coe's traditions and principles and devotion to quality, while helping it to evolve during the latter half of the twentieth century, when the pace of building products development and related machinery innovation and implementation became a world class sprint. We worked hard, we worked unafraid, we were fortunate to experience some good timing, but by no means was it always smooth sailing. It's a formula many successful American businesses have subscribed to, and one that Coe had adhered to since its beginning, which, like I stated, was way before I entered the picture. By the time I went to work for Coe at its headquarters in

Painesville, Ohio in the latter part of 1947, the company was already ninety-five years old. Coe's story was already embedded in the explosion of American industrial and manufacturing ingenuity through three major wars, including one war when our country fought itself. It never entered my mind back then that I would one day purchase the company, nearly thirty years later in December 1976. By then Coe Company operated an additional manufacturing facility in Portland, Oregon, which I had a hand in establishing. But I am getting ahead of myself here.

Coe was already over sixty years old when I was born on November 12, 1923 in Alexandria, Indiana, the son of a farmer, Mahlon Fields, and his wife, Ethel. Alexandria, which is in Madison County, is about forty-five miles northeast of Indianapolis. Its population today is maybe seven thousand. It was a lot less back then. I was the newest of six siblings at the time, with two still to come after me. My older brothers were Everett, Robert and Eugene. My older sisters were Louise and Marienne. My younger brother was Donald and a younger sister was Betty Jean. All of them are gone except for Donald and myself.

My father grew up in a town called Cicero, Indiana, about twenty miles north of Indianapolis. Most of his family had moved to Indiana back in the 1870s and 1880s and they were the first settlers in the area where my family lived. All of his relatives grew up in that area and in Tipton County. His dad, my grandfather, had a farm in Elwood, six or seven miles from our home. My mother's father and mother, Will and Lennie Myerly, had a very nice farm several miles from where we lived. My grandfather was always a big help to my parents with their farm. So they were all farmers and everybody helped each other in the farming business as farmers do. It was a hard working, farming family. Nobody had any money. If they did, they hid it well, and when they died it didn't turn up.

When I was born we were living on the farm my father had rented. I don't remember much about it. He then bought a farm of one-hundred acres in 1927 when I was four. He had a very sizable mortgage and during the ensuing depression we raised most of our food. We had plenty to eat, but dad had a heck of a time making his mortgage payment.

When I was five I remember very well that dad had built a new barn, which he could barely afford in the first place, but it was really a beauty. After a year or two the barn burned to the ground. We had cut hay for the summer which was grown for our cattle and horses. And in this case we had cut the hay and it was laying down on the ground when it rained a little before we had a chance to bring it in out of the field. We brought it in a little too wet and it was packed in the hay mow in the barn. The hot summer heat caused it to catch on fire as a result of internal combustion. The barn burned down before we could do anything about it. There was no fire department within miles and fighting the fire with no facilities was a lost cause. I will always remember while it burned, lying down in the back of our house and hearing my dad crying because it broke his heart, having put so much of his savings into it. This was just before the Great Depression, and when the depression came along we had no resources to rebuild it.

During the depression my dad was able to secure a job with General Motors at the Delco Division as a machinist. It was still a very difficult time for our family. Almost all the money he made at General Motors he paid against the mortgage. A banker came to us on a pretty regular basis because we couldn't make all the payments and dad would beg the banker to let us work it out. I don't think the bank wanted the farm either—what would they do with it?—so they went along with him. We didn't have to move and my dad kept struggling and after many years paid down the mortgage. I can now appreciate that situation. I was on the U.S. Bank Board for seventeen years and spent time on the credit committee. I used to review in the credit committee how the bank tried to push people with bad mortgages to pay up. The bank didn't want the land or the farm. What were they going to do with it? They'd do everything they could to help the borrower satisfy the mortgage. It's still the same way today. Maybe it isn't obvious, but the banks really try hard to help the borrower, but on the other hand the government has loan requirements of the banker and they review on a monthly basis non-paying loans. If a borrower is paying interest on a loan, that may be acceptable, but if they aren't paying interest and aren't paying anything, the bank has to foreclose. The banks needed the money and yet they didn't want the collateral.

My dad was a hard worker. He worked day and night, General Motors, the farm, Saturdays and Sundays. We had enough income to pay for the mortgage and to keep ourselves in clothes during the depression. But it was pretty drastic. You can't imagine not having a nickel to buy a candy bar or ten cents to go to a movie. That just didn't exist in those days. I know we were always worried about going broke. We saw many other people who had gone broke. We never went broke, but we were so close to it we could touch it. So through the years for me there was always that sense of looking back to those years and being worried about going broke and fearful of being unsuccessful.

I was born in 1923 and the depression hit in 1929 to 1933. I don't remember too much about it, other than we didn't have much in the way of resources. As we all later learned in school and in the history books, the value of stock on the New York Stock Exchange was less than a fifth of what it had been at its peak in 1929, prior to the October stock market crash. At one point one out of every four Americans was unemployed.

I knew we couldn't afford to buy coal, the main source of heat in those days. We didn't have electricity. At the back side of our farm was the main line of the railroad. They switched cars and sometimes they would be switching at a pretty slow rate. Some of the neighbors would jump the freight trains and throw coal off the coal cars into the side ditch and then go back and gather it up in a burlap bag. I can remember them doing that and I can remember one of them falling under the train and having his legs cut off.

In those days there were a lot of tramps or hobos who were jumping freight trains and oftentimes they would fight and one would throw the other off. Several of them came to our house for handouts. I remember one came and was bloody from his head to his waist. Somebody had beaten him up, broken all his teeth out and he was crying. Mother provided water for him and he went on down the road. Those incidents served as a reminder that our lives could have been worse.

I began farming around the age of 10. My older brothers Everett and Robert were young married guys and they had gone on their own. My sister Louise had attended Anderson College and become a secretary with Container Corp. My other older sister, Marienne, was an invalid who was never able to attend school. She had infantile paralysis at birth. She was a very sweet person and always stayed close to my sister Louise. They moved to Cincinnati and Marienne became involved with other disabled people and became their eyes and ears and doing things for them that they were incapable of doing for themselves. She became the 1981 Woman of the Year in Cincinnati, which was quite a feat for a person with those disabilities and problems. At the time she was Chairwoman of the Cincinnati Coalition of People with Disabilities. She made the best of what she had, and liked to give back.

So it was left to me and my brother Eugene, who was 12, to farm the one-hundred acres. He would drive the horses and I would steer the plow. There were no tractors early on. We had five horses, some cattle and mother always raised 200 to 300 chickens each year. We did the obvious things. We plowed the land, we milked the cows and fed the pigs. We didn't have any sheep. We did have a few geese. We had a two acre garden and about five acres in orchard. We couldn't afford to buy coal for heating our house, but we burned corn instead. We had no electricity, no running water except we did have a windmill that pumped water from a well that supplied water for drinking for the horses and cattle and other livestock.

Farm equipment in those days was very antiquated by any standards. It was always pretty worn out or broken down and it was always a challenge to keep it repaired to where it would operate effectively. Learning in those days to maintain equipment and harness for the horses, and all those things I had to do on the farm was really a learning experience. I learned how to do things in the simplest ways and those were the things that stuck with me for the rest of my life. We couldn't afford to buy new equipment so we had to do with what we had. If something broke down we had to find a way of maintaining it to where it could go on and get the job done. Maintaining a lot of broken down equipment was very difficult. We had to use baling wire and a sledgehammer to repair things to a state that would help us get through. One of the difficult things was the horse harness, the leather work used to put on a horse and the collar and the strappings. They were always in a state of disrepair for one reason or another. They wore out or the hot sun baked them to the point where they became brittle. Repairing the harness for the horses was an ongoing issue.

I had to keep the plow shears sharpened. Once they became dull they didn't plow very well, so it fell into my scope of things to do to take them to a blacksmith and he would heat them to a high temperature and pound them into a new shape to sharpen them.

We always had trouble with discs, with keeping bearings in a disc. In those days there weren't anti-friction bearings. They were what were called boxen bearings and they consisted of melted babbitt, as it is softer than copper. We had to set those up in a mold, heat the metal and pour them into the mold and then remove them and place them in the supports for the discs. That was a continuing problem as bearings wore out fast and you had to repeat the process twice or three times during a farming year. There were quite a few tricks to do that, and being a young kid you constantly thought of burning your feet or your hands in the process of pouring the hot babbitt.

In later years, in the late 30s, my dad was able to buy the first tractor in the county. He bought it for my brother and me. That was a new Farmall F-12 International. It had lugged wheels. It was pretty fancy for we boys. My brother and I used the tractor not only to farm our farm, but other people's adjacent farms who didn't have the wherewithal to buy a tractor, so we helped them and made a few dollars doing job work. Of course our problems magnified when we got the tractor. We did everything faster so we broke up the equipment faster. It had an internal combustion engine and we came to know the tractor well, the hard way.

My brother and I were fortunate we didn't seriously hurt ourselves during those years. The worst injury I had was when he cut up my thumb pretty bad. I was holding a pumpkin and he had a corn knife, a big long knife, fourteen to sixteen inches long and he was chopping the pumpkin to feed the cattle; we couldn't give it to them whole but in smaller pieces. Anyway he caught my thumb with the knife but did not break anything.

I guess the worst injury on our farm happened to my father. It was dark in the middle of winter and he was feeding the horses. We always had cats around the barn and a cat ran between the legs of this horse and the horse let go with a big kick and my father happened to be right in line with the hoof and caught it in the ribs. Broke five ribs. I thought he was dying on the spot. He could hardly breathe or move. Another one of life's experiences.

As far as I was concerned, every other boy and girl in the community were having to do the same things. We weren't doing anything more than working and helping with the family as we tried to live a reasonable life. We had plenty to eat. We had fried chicken two or three times a week. It was my favorite. I love fried chicken even today. My mother had a huge vegetable garden and had two acres of potatoes each year. We had an orchard and raised apples and peaches with all other sorts of fruit. We sold part of our crops, but most of the corn, wheat and oats we raised was used to feed the livestock. We sold livestock to generate a little cash. Mother sold surplus eggs from her chickens. We butchered a calf and maybe two, two-hundred pound pigs a year. That was always an experience. A lot of hard work goes into cutting up that pig and rendering fat into lard. It was a lot of fun when you were a kid, out in the snow, the cold, the big blazing fire and cooking all the renderings, the fat of the hog. It was an exciting time and very interesting in the cutting process.

We were very disciplined and church going, though sometimes not too regular in the wintertime. We had to walk about two miles to church so cold weather limited our attendance. I can't ever remember seeing a glass of wine or whiskey in the house. We went to school regularly and I think I missed one day of school in eight years of my elementary school years. There were days when I had a bad cold or pneumonia, but we spent a lot of time outdoors, temperatures could get down to twenty-five below zero but those cows and other livestock had to be taken care of, so you had to get out there and get it done.

Mother took care of the discipline around the house; my dad took care of discipline around the farm. The discipline we had was related to our chores. There were always many many jobs to do. We had to clean the stables, had to milk the cows, had to harness the horses, had to feed the horses and cows. The discipline came from doing all those chores we had to do at certain times of the day. My dad was pretty level headed most of the time. He'd get mad because some of the cattle would break out into the road, and he was sort of bossy with the kids from time to time, but obviously we needed some direction.

At bedtime we were always dead tired. When dinner was over we had a radio and we would listen to Amos and Andy, Lum and Abner and a couple of other programs then we went to bed. We also listened to afternoon ballgames on the radio. We lived about halfway between Cincinnati and Chicago. My favorite team was the Cubs, but if they weren't playing, I'd switch to the Reds. We received the Indianapolis and Anderson newspapers and read about them. The Cubs had some good teams in the 1930s, winning several pennants. Charlie Grimm was their manager. They had Hack Wilson and Gabby Hartnett. The Reds weren't bad either, winning back-to-back pennants in 1939-1940. I remember Johnny Vander Meer pitching consecutive no-hitters in 1937. Ernie Lombardi and Paul Derringer were a couple of the Reds' stars.

As for politics, we had some discussion but it didn't mean too much, other than I learned that my mother was a Democrat and my father was a Republican. We followed Wendell Willkie's career. He was the presidential candidate for the Republican Party in 1940, and had grown up about four miles from us in Elwood. His wife and my sister had gone to the same school and my brother knew him in the earlier years. Though he lost to Roosevelt, Willkie won more votes than any previous Republican candidate. The interesting thing is that he had been a Democrat his entire career, switching parties in 1939 in opposition to the New Deal.

I also remember "unions" being the topic of some conversations. I can't tell you for sure whether was my dad was in the union or not. He used to argue against it but I'm not sure if he had to join. I don't really think so. That was right after the depression and before the war. The automobile business was just getting embedded in the communities and generating a meaningful source of employment for people, so they weren't unionizing nearly as much as other industries. The coal miners unions were always in the headlines. For some reason, the coal miners and west coast longshoremen had a bad reputation. My dad wasn't sure he wanted to join a group of hoodlums, which is what they were known as in those days.

Speaking of hoodlums, I remember as a boy hearing about the exploits of the gangster, John Herbert Dillinger. He was born in Indianapolis and his family moved to Mooresville which is where he began his life of crime, and then he robbed a grocery store in Martinsville, only to be apprehended and sentenced to prison. He was released after eight years and fell right into the Great Depression, and picked up right where he had left off. Dillinger and his gang began a streak of bank robberies across Indiana in towns such as Daleville, Montpelier, Indianapolis, Greencastle, East Chicago, South Bend and others outside of Indiana but in the vicinity. He was later arrested and charged with the murder of a police officer in East Chicago, and held in the Crown Point jail. This was the famous instance when he carved a wooden gun in his cell and used it to trick a guard into opening his cell and escaping. After more crime spree, a "madam" from Gary, Indiana made a deal with the FBI to set up

Dillinger as he and the "lady in red" left a movie theater on Chicago's North Side. He was shot and killed in a nearby alley as he tried to out-run the authorities. This was in 1934; I was eleven at the time.

But we didn't sit around the table and talk about current events very much. We had too many things to do. Dad got up at five to do his part, feed the cows and horses, and by quarter till seven he was on his way to work at General Motors. We'd get up about six and do our chores, get washed up and eat breakfast and off to school. And the minute we got home from school we had things to do. In the winter we had to shovel snow, make sure the windmill was operating to pump water for the livestock, go break ice in the water tank because the livestock wouldn't break it with their noses. It made for a long day, but that was life and we lived with it. We didn't sit around and just talk unless it was a very snowy day and we couldn't get out for work.

CHAPTER TWO

A YOUNG MAN'S PATH

I don't want to make it sound like I didn't have a life other than the farm. It's just that the farm and the chores were first and foremost, and everything else was planned around it. I attended Alexandria High School and naturally had a gang of kids I ran around with. I lived about four miles from the school, and if I wanted to do something other than ride the school bus, I either had to hitchhike or walk. That wasn't too bad in the summertime, but in the winter in twenty degrees below zero, walking home for several miles was somewhat of a chore. It was a good thing if in your group somebody had a Model T Ford and could pick you up so you didn't have to walk everywhere. We had such a person in our group, Bruce Beebee. He was a neighbor and a little bit older, and quite an innovative guy. He taught me to drive that Model T and push all those pedals on the floor. He eventually graduated to a Model A Ford. We were typical kids. We would enjoy riding around and do some pranking at Halloween time, play basketball on Saturday afternoon, and had lots of good, wholesome fun.

My father didn't have a car. Well, he had an old car, back from the 20s, that we stored in the barn, but mother wouldn't let him drive. They didn't have hardly any roads in those days and it wasn't difficult to find a side ditch to run into. I think during his driving days that my father had discovered his share of ditches. My father rode to work on the bus that GM sent out for its employees.

So mother actually purchased our first car for my brother and I. I think I was a junior in high school, around 1939. It was a 1937 Pontiac. It wasn't very good but it was better than walking. I didn't actually buy my first car until after the war, in 1946, a 1941 Oldsmobile, and then when I went to work for Coe in 1947 I bought a 1947 Pontiac.

I played basketball and football in high school. Like I said, I had to work that in with farming the farm. I played forward in basketball and played guard or center in football. I was just average. Basketball was big in Indiana of course. There were a lot of good people in basketball around our part of the state, people who became national figures. John Wooden came from Tipton, about eighteen miles away. I was only four or five when he played at Martinsville and they won the state championship and finished runner-up twice. He was a three time All State selection and people were very proud as he advanced through his legendary coaching career, particularly at UCLA. His record as a coach was so tremendous, ten national titles at UCLA, seven of them in a row, that people forget he was a great college basketball player at Purdue University, an All-American guard for three years. He played professionally in the National Basketball League as it was called then for the Indianapolis team, coached high school basketball for a number of years, and then coached Indiana State University for two years, before going to UCLA.

Another Indiana basketball legend in our area was Everett Case, who was born in nearby Anderson, and coached Frankfort High to four state high school championships in the 20s and 30s and then became the head coach at North Carolina State University and won numerous conference championships. Case is really credited for leading the Atlanta Coast Conference into the national limelight and creating the basketball spirit that's identified with the ACC today. The states of North Carolina and Louisiana had decided they wanted to start emphasizing basketball and they hired several very good coaches from the state of Indiana.

Another Hall of Famer was Cliff Wells, who coached at Bloomington and Logansport high schools, won several state championships, and went on to coach Tulane University for many years. And there was Branch McCracken, who had played high school ball at Monrovia High School, then coached Ball State, my old school, for a number of years before taking over at the University of Indiana, which won two national titles under his guidance.

If you've gotten the impression that I like basketball, well I do, and I still follow it closely today, especially the pros, and I like to attend the Portland Trail Blazers games. I always enjoyed football, too. I was a pretty big kid for those days, the days of the leather helmets. I went on to play football my freshman year at Ball State, which was the only year I was there. Ball State has come a long way as a football program since then. They can play with about anybody now.

Along with farming and playing sports during my high school years, I worked regularly during the summer months. My first job was working on a highway construction crew. I was a pick and shovel guy. Then I went to work for Johns Manville, which had a rock wool plant in my hometown, which seemed to be a center for rock wool plants. Both Johns Manville and National Gypsum had plants there. I was a cupulo tender; that's where you take the gypsum rock, which is fairly soft, you heated that to a point of melting and let this hot rock pour down over a V shaped angle iron and drip off into a high pressure steam jet oven. It becomes airborne and floats down onto this wide conveyor and as it cools it makes a mat or whatever you're making, a wool or a mat. They mixed it with some fire retardant and it was blown down onto a conveyor that conveyed it to an area where it was put into a bag. I ran two cupulos. I think there were five in the plant and they had a very experienced operator on the other three. He taught me to run the other two and if I had problems I called on him for help.

Then the next summer I got a job at Alladin Lamp Company. They were in the glass business and made lamp fixtures and thermos bottles. My job was to work with the maintenance superintendent and I was sort of a gopher. He would lay out the work that had to be done and I would supervise the maintenance people to see that the work was done properly. Even though I didn't know too much about it, it was good experience because the main superintendent gave me a lot of latitude and I enjoyed what I was doing. Maintaining glass blow equipment is certainly an experience you wouldn't get anywhere else—blowing hot glass through a big tube, probably an inch and a half diameter, six or seven feet long. You reach in and get a gob of hot glass and blow it into the end of this tube and if you know what you're doing you can form many different shapes and configurations.

I attended Ball State right out of high school in 1941. I had gone to Ball State with no particular purpose in mind other than it was near home and it was a place I thought I could afford to go. It was less than thirty miles away. My father had the farm taking care of itself fairly well by 1941. We were making a little money. My mother scrimped and saved to provide the tuition and I worked at school in restaurants and I shoveled ashes out of the boiler room at the central boiler house that kept the buildings warm at Ball State. It meant getting up at four in the morning and it was a back-breaking job, but it was a steady paying job. I lived in a boarding house. My mother did all the laundry and I continued to do my share on the farm in taking care of the livestock. I also worked an afternoon shift at Owens Illinois glass company. I inspected glass bottles, beer bottles and sorting them was a laborious task, making sure there were no defects in the glass.

During that summer I got a job with General Motors at the

plant in Anderson, about twelve miles from home. They had buses to go to certain areas to pick up employees and I rode the bus to work. I operated an automatic engine lathe for machining generator shafts. There were two or three bearing points on that shaft that had to be ground to a very precise dimension. It was an automatic machine and it would grind the surface area to precise dimensions but someone had to take the part out of the machine and replace it with an unfinished part. I was in charge of that machine for several months. The next summer I was fortunate to go back to General Motors and I ran an external Norton grinder which ground certain parts of the generator shaft or a starter shaft or many different parts that needed the same type of machining treatment.

Ball State was a teacher's college and I enjoyed being there but I learned that being a teacher probably wasn't my cup of tea. I didn't think it was enough of a challenge for me. There wasn't much in the way of arithmetic and physics and those sorts of things that appealed to me as I grew up, as I was learning to be a mechanic and maintaining old, rusty equipment. I had a chance to go to Indiana University the next year and did that for a year, and was in the ROTC program. I was influenced by several local friends who had gone to Indiana and they encouraged me to go there. I enjoyed it very much. And then at the end of my second year at Indiana, I was drafted into the service. My older brother, Gene, had already volunteered to go into the service and was in the 82nd Airborne Division. I had a choice of where I wanted to go, and I chose the U.S. Air Force.

I served 42 months in the Air Force. I reported for basic training at Clearwater, Florida, and after going through that I applied for cadet school, flying school, to become a pilot. But at the time the cadet school was full. They tried to take those guys like myself and put them in supplemental education programs that would help them when they got into flying school. They sent me to Chanute Field in Rantoul, Ill., adjacent Champagne and the University of Illinois. This was a flight training school to teach pilots navigation and instrument flying with simulators. About the time I got through, the cadet school had opened up and they sent me to the Air Force training center at Wichita Falls, Texas and at that point I went through advanced basic training, and when I finished, the cadet school had closed again. They had more than they could handle. Everybody wanted to fly but they just didn't have enough airplanes and training bases to accommodate the candidates. They then sent me to an Army training center at Oklahoma State in Stillwater, the ASTP program. That was an educational program and we studied there just as if we were in college, taking courses in math, chemistry, physics. Then at some point they decided to close the institution and send everyone to another ASTP program at Rhode Island State College at Kingston. I studied a year there and lived in a dormitory as if in regular college. That was a very good engineering school and that's where I got my strong urge to ultimately become an engineer. We pretty much did all the things you would do at a normal university. It was a lot of fun. We marched from one class to another in platoons. I was a platoon leader, not that it made me special, but I had the responsibility of looking after fifteen to twenty guys and if they got in trouble I was in trouble with them.

At that period of the war they were preparing for the big push into Western Europe, which was not known to any of us. They shut down the ASTP program at Rhode Island State and sent us all to camp in Blackstone, Virginia. We joined the 77th Lightning Division, an Army infantry division. We had a very concentrated infantry basic training, which included live fire, crawling under barbed wire fences, difficult and tough training, all of which I didn't mind at all. I had always been involved in athletics and I was in good shape. Then one day they announced we were going to be shipped overseas and had two days to get our private affairs in order. The night before we were to ship out everyone was at the entertainment center being treated with a band and live entertainment. Most of us huddled around as we tried to figure out what was going on and where we were going, but we knew the 77th Lightning Division was going to be in the middle of whatever was going to happen. About ten o'clock at night the loudspeaker came on and paged me and one other fella, Clint Courtney, to report to company headquarters right away. They said we both had special serial numbers that identified us as being capable of being instructors of Link training and instrument flying and we were going to be shipped out to Charleston, South Carolina to train pilots in navigation and instrument flying. It was just at the last minute. I didn't know many of the fellas in the 77th division, but I understand that most of them were wiped out in the invasion of Normandy. They were the first group to land. Oh fate, I should say. I reflect on it every once in a while.

One soldier who participated in the invasion was my brother Gene. He landed behind the lines on the day of the invasion and had been on the ground two or three days when they were ambushed. He got shot up pretty bad with shrapnel in his chest and stomach. They dragged him into a field hospital. It so happened that my older sister's friend was a field nurse in the same field hospital and she saved his life. Her name was Ursulla and as she was looking over the roster of all the people in that hospital she ran across his name. She literally pulled him out of a pile of bodies and got him to an operating table. They got him patched up well enough to transport him to a more effective hospital. He was awarded the Purple Heart. It was just a miracle that she happened to be glancing through the roster. Gene recovered. He had a lot of scars, but he was active throughout his life. He didn't like to talk about it much

I wasn't at Charleston long. Since I had been away from the flight training school for some time, they shipped me off to an advanced instrument flying school to become re-trained. This was at Bryant Field at Texas A&M, College Station, Texas. I went through this program for about three months so by then I had about seven months of training in instrument flying and navigation. Then I was sent back to Charleston Air Base and began re-training pilots coming back from the Europe Theater who had been in the Fifth and Eighth Air Force. We re-trained them with modern instrument flying techniques and new equipment in preparation for the Asian Theater. It was very interesting talking with these pilots who had been over in Europe and had all those hair raising experiences. Many of their pals had not made it. Our instrument flying technology was the newest that was available at the time. There wasn't very much instrument flying during the early parts of the war, but there were various levels of it late in 1945 and 1946. We taught both basic and advanced Link training, and I spent the rest of my Army years instructing instrument flying at Charleston.

The Air Transport Command had a football team in 1946 and I played football with ATC in Nashville, Tennessee. During that year the various Air Force generals had football teams, including the First Air Force, Second, Third and Fourth Air Force, Air Transport Command, Navy PreFlight, Strategic Air Command, seven or eight football teams. Everybody wanted to go to the football camp to get out of normal military duty. We had four-hundred guys show up for training camp and boiled it down to about fifty. We practiced out at Berry Field, near an old mansion on the back side of the Nashville airport. We played our home games at Vanderbilt Stadium. It was a wonderful season.

Then I was shipped back to Charleston and was there three or four weeks, then moved to Romulus Field in the Detroit area and that's where I was processed and prepared for discharge and sent home.

My father had died of pneumonia in 1944 while I was stationed in Charleston. I didn't get home in time before he passed away. He was 60. He was still working for General Motors and was farming. He never smoked. But in those days it wasn't uncommon to have tuberculosis and he probably had a touch of it along with pneumonia. He wasn't a big man like myself. He wasn't all that healthy. He always worked hard and expected everybody else to work hard. That was an important lesson that I learned from him.

CHAPTER THREE

<u>INTRODUCTION TO COE</u>

So I had bounced around quite a bit and during the service years I had probably two years worth of education. After the service I attended Purdue University for a very productive year. I didn't have enough credits for a degree, but I had five to six years of concentrated schooling. I decided that if I could get a good job that summer that showed promise I should take it. Jobs were hard to find in those days with a lot of boys coming back from war and reclaiming jobs they had before they went into the service. I had spent almost six years getting an education and was anxious to get on with my life. I needed a few odd credits but taking another year to graduate seemed too much.

When I got out of the service in 1946, mother had been leasing out the farm to another farmer, which generated some good income for her. After they finished the farm work for that year I began farming the farm again and started taking classes at Purdue. Mother was still very healthy and certainly very vibrant. I was happy to be home, but I wasn't interested making a career out of farming. I was determined to apply the many life lessons I had learned on the farm and in the service, and even from those summer jobs, toward something different, while generating some income for myself in post-war America.

After I had returned home from service and a year at Purdue, I was farming the farm and meanwhile National Gypsum was building a rock wool plant in the area. I just by happenstance met the superintendent of the construction company that was building this plant. He was a wiry old guy and probably took a drink or two, but he was very much in command of this construction project. The construction company was called Kirby Sanders Construction Company. They were about half complete with this project and their superintendent asked me if I was looking for a job, and that he had one that may not be very interesting for me, but it was surveying on a big sewer project. I said I don't care what it is, I'm farming a farm now and I'm looking for a job that pays good enough. He said we'll pay you four-hundred dollars a month and you start tomorrow. I said fine and I went to the project the next day. This plant occupied forty acres and it was located fairly near a good size creek that flooded, so they had to have a storm sewer that consisted of a six foot diameter pipe, and this was the main storm sewer that was going to carry the water off the land where the plant was located, so as not to allow the floor of the plant to flood during the spring rains.

They had a chief engineer and his name was Tommy and it turned out he was a flighty sort of a guy and as wild as a march hare. He would come to work some days and other days he wouldn't. He would get too drunk to come to work. He was out of the same ilk as the superintendent, but the superintendent was always at work. Even if he was half drunk, he was still seeing that the job was moving. I was down on the sewer project one day and the old man, the superintendent, showed up, and he had a Kaiser automobile, robin egg blue and you couldn't miss it two miles away. He showed up and he came to me and said I have another job for you, I just fired Tommy and you've got his job. I said what does it involve. He said it involves everybody on the job, the ironworkers, the plumbers, the painters, laborers, electricians and anybody who works here. You've got to take it over and do his job. Fortunately it was about three quarters finished and I really enjoyed it. He had some confidence I could do the job and I finished the job.

During this process we were installing a lot of new machinery that was designed by engineers from Coe Manufacturing. The plant was to manufacture rock wool batts, which became insulating material that's formed into eighteen-inch squares. You'll remember that I had worked in Johns Manville's rock wool plant one summer when I was in college. I had been the cupulo tender, and like that plant, this new one had a cupulo that would blow this cotton like material into a big bake oven. This material had to be heated and kept heated while it cooled down and got into a form and shape that would maintain its configuration. It would come out in a big blanket that might be ten feet wide and maybe three inches thick, and at that point this rock wool blanket would be cut into eighteen-inch squares, boxed up and shipped to construction sites. At this plant the big oven was made by Coe Manufacturing. The oven was the biggest machine in the plant. It was a new design, and Coe's chief engineer was there quite often to make sure everything was fitting properly and designed according to specifications.

The main designer from Coe was a fella named Ed Parker, about seventy years old, just the salt of the earth and a brilliant engineer. He was on the job maybe half the time and when it came to lunch hour I always saw to it to go by and see if he would go to lunch with me. So we went to lunch together nearly every day he was on the job and we became well acquainted. I saw to it that he had the proper people on the job where he was supervising part of the machinery installation, so he was appreciative and when his job was complete, he said if you're ever looking for a job, let me know as I think our company would be well advised to hire you. I said this sounds interesting but I've got to finish this job. He said I understand, there's no hurry.

Maybe a month later I called him to say the job was complete and he said, well, I'm coming to Alexandria this next week and if you'd like why don't you pack up a bag as I'll be returning after a couple of days on the job and you can come back with me to Painesville, Ohio. I'll introduce you to the people you should meet and maybe it'll work out. I did just that and that's the way I became acquainted with Coe. When I arrived there to interview for the job, Mr. Frank Milbourn, Sr., who was the owner and chairman, and up in his 70s, described the position to me and finally said what kind of money are you making young fellow. I said I was making four-hundred dollars a month. He said we can't afford to pay that. I said what are you offering. He said we're offering three-hundred dollars. I said I'll take it as the amount was not that important when starting out with a new company. If you did good work and continued to do so, the money would come. Plus, three-hundred dollars was still good pay in those days. This was in November 1947. I was just turning 24 years old. They put me in the engineering department. I had a drafting board, pencil and paper, and there I was, beginning my 53-year relationship with Coe Manufacturing Company.

It didn't take me long to learn, and see with my own eyes, that Coe had a brilliant history under its belt. And based on the people I had met and seeing their devotion to the company and its equipment, it didn't take me long to realize that Coe also had the potential to experience a great future. I had fallen in with a very special company.

CHAPTER FOUR

THE HISTORY OF COE
(PART ONE)

The following material borrows liberally from several histo-
ries of Coe, including one written by Frank Milbourn, Jr.,
whose family purchased the company and ultimately sold it to
me.

Coe's hometown of Painesville, Ohio is located thirty miles
northeast of Cleveland, off Lake Erie in Lake County. It was
once known as Oak Openings because it was just that, an opening in the oak woods. It received its present name in honor of
Revolutionary War General Edward Paine, who was one of the
first to settle there. Early farmers could earn thirty-seven cents a
cord by hauling logs to the local charcoal-making furnaces. In
1835, the Arcole Furnace in nearby Madison kept two hundred
men busy rain or shine seven days a week cutting down trees for
charcoal. Besides the furnaces, there were forges, asheries for
making potash, tanneries, sawmills and factories that turned out

manufactured wood products.

Among all of this thriving industry, another manufacturing company was born. Harold Hayes Coe was only twenty-one years old when he joined with Leonard Anderson to build The Anderson and Coe Company at Jackson and St. Clair streets in Painesville. The year was 1852. They advertised themselves in the local newspaper as "Manufacturers of Steam Engines, Machinery, Sawmill, Shop and Grist Mill Engines."

Harold Hayes Coe grew up in Austinburg, then a frontier lumber center east of Painesville. The young Coe and his mother, Polly, were said to be slave runners on the Underground Railroad. He would be hustled out of bed to hitch up his lumber wagon to run a load of shivering slaves down to Ashtabula Harbor, under cover of darkness, to catch a boat for Canada. Later, he was one of five thousand who heard President-elect Lincoln speak in Painesville en route to Washington for the inauguration, and was among the first in Lake County to answer Lincoln's call for volunteers for the Civil War. He was a leader of the Regimental Band of the Seventh Ohio Infantry. He returned to become a prominent Painesville citizen, twice elected major and serving one term as county treasurer.

The fledgling business of Anderson and Coe had no sooner been established when the area's logging force, as the timber resource contracted, began moving on to Michigan and Wisconsin. To make matters worse, in 1857 the nation went into a full-scale Panic. The failure of the New York branch of the Ohio Life Insurance and Trust Co. set off the panic. British investors removed funds from American banks. Grain prices fell dramatically. Manufactured goods began to pile up in warehouses. Widespread railroad failures occurred. And 30,000 pounds of gold were lost at sea in a shipment from the San Francisco Mint to eastern banks. Public confidence soured on the government's ability to back its paper currency with gold. Lake County was hit hard. Businesses and homes foreclosed and sheriff's sales became common. But The Anderson and Coe Company prevailed. It set a precedent for the company that would help it through many economic downturns in the wood products trade. It developed a new machine.

Anderson receives credit for inventing the company's rotary lathe. Due to the economy and the absence of suitable trees for sawn lumber, many sawmills were converting to making baskets, boxes, spools and staves for barrels. Anderson and Coe's new lathe was able to convert timber blocks into the varied thicknesses and widths of veneer. The local paper declared that one of the company's "most wonderful inventions is a machine for making of slack barrel staves which could cut 125,000 staves in 10 hours." Despite the adverse economy, the company began to prosper, until the Civil War broke out. Harold Coe left in 1861 to fight for the Union. The war depleted Lake County of men, money and resources, but Anderson managed to keep the company alive during the five bleak years Coe was gone. H. H. Coe lost two small daughters while he was away, but he came back to Painesville determined to rebuild his life and livelihood. He returned in 1865 and immediately took on a new partner, Fredric Wilkes, who bought out Anderson. The company became Coe-Wilkes.

Wilkes was an engineer and inventor. He had served an apprenticeship as a clerk at the Arcole Furnace in Madison in the 1830s, the largest business in the Western Reserve at the time. He moved to another furnace in Lowellsville, Ohio in 1845, which he converted to burning raw, soft coal for smelting pig iron, the first furnace in the United States to do so; and in the process helped save much of Ohio's remaining timber from being converted to charcoal for the furnaces.

Wilkes came back to Lake County in 1850 to convert The Geauga Furnace Company to coal-burning, and stayed, subsequently operating a furnace at the top of the hill just a few blocks from Anderson and Coe on what was known as Furnace Hill. But Lake County's limited supply of iron ore was also running out in the late 60s, and Wilkes was ready for something new.

The Coe-Wilkes Company blossomed in the postbellum boom as construction and reconstruction spiraled the demand for lumber and sawmill machinery. The Mississippi River was jammed with logs headed for the treeless Plains States. The cross-country railroads were built, one under the leadership of Painesville based General Casement, opening up the Pacific Northwest to logging. Coe-Wilkes began to ship machinery farther and farther from Painesville. In 1867, it had eight employees; in 1869, eighteen were on the payroll.

In 1870, the year John D. Rockefeller incorporated Standard Oil in Cleveland, natural gas was discovered in Lake County and Painesville put in street lights. A group of local businessmen approached the Coe-Wilkes Company with a need for thin wood tapers that could be used to light the lamps. Coe and Wilkes set to work on their original rotary lathe. They improved it to the point that it could take a section of a log and cut a thin sheet of veneer approximately one-eighth inch thick that would unroll from the log. This, together with a clipper to cut the wood into strips, furnished the tapers the "Old Lamplighter" used on his rounds.

The first local "Rotary Cutting Veneer Machine and Clipper" was installed in 1870 in a plant owned by Charles Pratt on the west bank of the Grand River. Pratt soon discovered that he could also make toothpicks with his new machines, and turned out so many of them—at least until the local scrub oaks ran out—that the place became known as "Toothpick Hill."

The new lathe helped extend the life of many local wood industries by allowing a more economical, conservative use of the remaining native timbers. The Robinson Basket Company on the Grand River in Painesville survived into the 1900s as one of the largest manufacturers of grape baskets in the world. In 1900, it advertised the addition of a new line of Coe veneer equipment as it shipped abroad five or six carloads of products a week.

So much timber was cut in Lake County in the late 1800s to feed the iron ore furnaces, forges, mills, asheries, tanneries, and to build roads and ships that Lake County became an agricultural economy as the land became cleared and cultivated. By the early 1900s, only 13,000 acres of woodland remained of the 89,000 acres of timberland that had originally comprised Lake County. The once thought inexhaustible supply of timber was about run out.

In 1891, Wilkes retired, declaring that "the lumbering days" were over. The company was forty years old. H. H. Coe was 61 when he welcomed Harry P. Coe, his only son, age 26, into the business, which then became The Coe Manufacturing Company. The younger Coe was different from his father. "Handsome Harry" favored wine, women and horses, and was twice divorced. But Harry had a flair for selling, and the company prospered so much that it outgrew its quarters.

1901 was a peak year for Coe. The Coe rotary veneer lathe won a Gold Medal at the Pan-American Exposition in Buffalo and the company broke ground for a new plant. It had purchased five acres on Bank Street at the Nickel Plate Railroad. Everything put into the plant was the newest and best. Natural gas fired the boilers. The very latest in arc and electric lights was used in the shops and office. The payroll jumped to thirty-two employees.

But a year later, in 1902, the nation entered a deep depression that was to last over a decade. Harry was undaunted. He advertised in the 1902 *Woodworker*, "HERE'S THE PROPOSITION...Come to Painesville, Ohio (a most centrally located place) and see sights you never saw before pertaining to the cutting of veneers and thin lumber. And, if you are not completely awed with what you see, we will pay all your travel expenses."

At the fifty-year mark, The Coe Manufacturing Company had survived many vicissitudes and challenges. It had become well established, and possessed enthusiasm and momentum entering into the 20th century. From a general service shop, Coe now had a product line and direction. The business centered around the rotary veneer lathe and associated equipment. Veneer produced at this time fell into two categories: that needed for the furniture and plywood industries and that required for containers and packaging. Thin, high-grade, figured sheets were generated from such species as walnut, oak, mahogany and certain other rare woods. These sheets were glued together with thicker layers of hardwood that served as the core and back of multi-layered panels. Coe did design and build a few slicing machines to produce so-called figured, or fancy, veneers; however, slicers never became an important part of Coe's business. The rotary lathe, on the other hand, produced not only the thicker layers of hardwood needed for furniture panels, but when equipped with a "stay log" could handle cants to produce flitches of thin figured veneer.

Using more common woods of lesser value, such as pine and gum, the rotary lathe was capable of producing relatively thick veneers which, when cut to proper size and dried, could be made into such useful items as citrus and egg crates and for transporting other vegetable products. When cut in thinner thicknesses, basket slats could be produced from oak, elm, sycamore and other hardwoods, which, when woven, became baskets for berries, grapes and bananas.

As important as the rotary lathe was for The Coe Manufacturing Company in its early years, a second invention, largely attributed to H. H. Coe, had a great impact on the company's future. It was the roller veneer dryer. Drying the thin sheets of veneer as they left the lathe had always been the most difficult part of the process in making plywood, and no existing method was even adequate. Loft, rack and hanging sheets invariably resulted in a warped and split product. Coe's first dryer, which was built and sold in 1902, involved steel tubes (rollers) to move the veneer through the dryer, holding it flat and firm as the water was removed. The 1902 *Painesville Republican* advertised the Coe dryer as a "machine with no counterpart in the world." The concept involved a pair of rolls, the lower roll fixed and driven and the top roll floating and taking power through star gears at the other end. The conveying medium, enclosed by insulated panels and heated by warm recirculated air, proved to be an important "breakthrough" for the veneer and plywood industries. The pairs of rolls not only conducted heat much more efficiently, but also the ironing action as the material progressed through the dryer resulted in generally flat and far more acceptable sheets than were dried in racks, lofts or other manual methods. Another inherent advantage was the greatly reduced time for drying, which was in the range of minutes up to a half hour compared with days or weeks with the other methods.

At this time, the fortunes of The Coe Company were greatly enhanced by activities in the West. The Pacific Northwest was the lumber frontier. Trainloads of lumber were shipped East, bypassing shipments of machinery going West. In 1905, the Portland Manufacturing Company, a small wooden box operation and factory in the St. John's district of the city, was asked to produce something unusual from wood for the 100th anniversary celebration of the Lewis and Clark Expedition. Co-owner Gustav Carlson laminated wood panels from a variety of regional softwoods, using paint brushes as glue spreaders and house jacks as presses. Called "3-ply veneer work," the product created considerable interest among fairgoers, including several door, cabinet and trunk manufacturers who immediately placed orders. By 1907, Portland Manufacturing had installed an automatic glue spreader and a sectional hand press. Production soared to 420 panels a day. The construction-type plywood industry was born, which increased the demands for veneer lathes. Coe lathes were well represented in the early West Coast mills, and by 1912 the first Coe dryer was installed in a Washington plywood plant.

However, in 1908, H. H. Coe died and the company nearly followed him. His son, Harry P. Coe, who was a very aggressive, enthusiastic salesman, particularly with respect to the possibilities of the roller dryer, struggled through a then prevailing depression period. Stories persisted for years recalling Harry's way of doing business. As one story was told: A local contractor who had put the roof on the new Coe plant building approached Harry to collect two thousand dollars still owed him. Harry offered to match him double or nothing. But high-rolling could no longer save the company and Coe went into receivership. A lesser company might have disappeared, but Coe had, in more than sixty-five years, developed a sense of identity and purpose which was needed to survive.

In the midst of declining business, there occurred one momentary ray of hope that deserves mention. In 1909, the *Telegraph Republican* carried an exciting story regarding The Coe Manufacturing Company's activities. It stated, "This company is now loading the largest foreign order in its history. Twelve carloads, valued at $40,000, will leave here for New York City Monday, and will be delivered aboard boat to sail May 15 for Vladivostok, Siberia, the city made famous during the Japanese-Russian War. The shipment is consigned to the Skidelski Company, Russian manufacturers of veneers.

"There is a full line of veneer machinery, which includes two rotary machines, clippers, veneer saws, wringers, grinders, roller dry kiln, glue room machinery, presses, taping machines, jointers, veneer scrapers, and other minor parts to go to make up a modern veneer plant. The country where this big shipment is headed for is very rich in timber and surpasses, in this respect, any country or section of country on the globe. The order was secured several months ago when representatives of the Russian company visited this city."

The article also referred to Coe's new Veneer Re-Dryer. "Veneer users know only too well that no matter how well-dried green veneer may be, it in storage or transit reabsorbs moisture from the atmosphere. Before it can be used for purposes such as panels, furniture, piano work, etc., a redrying process to lower the moisture gathered must be a controlled amount." The article referred to Coe's general manager, W. H. Collier, and sales manager, R. N. Jernigan, as men well known for their ability, "and the affairs of the company could be entrusted to no better officers."

Then along came another war. World War I saw the entire woodworking machinery industry commandeered for the war effort. Coe, still run by managers and under receivership, devoted its facilities to making shell-turning lathes. The war left Coe depleted. It needed a strong leader to pick it up, dust it off, and set it on the road again.

CHAPTER FIVE

THE HISTORY OF COE
(PART TWO)

Coe was fortunate in that Frank W. Milbourn, Sr. arrived on the scene in 1920. He came to look at Coe right after the war. Born in Kentucky and graduated from the University of Kentucky at Lexington in mechanical engineering in 1901, he had spent all of his working life as an employee of Southern Engine and Boiler Works at Jackson, Tennessee, serving as engineer, traveling salesman, sales manager, and finally as vice president and general manager. He had traveled considerably himself, but mostly in the Southern states. Southern Engine and Boiler Works' best customers were sawmills in the Southern states, with a few more on the West Coast.

Milbourn was married, with a small son and a desire to have his own business. He walked through the Coe buildings that had not been painted in sixteen years. He saw the machinery and tools in poor condition, and he saw the state of the books. He also saw the potential.

Milbourn had done his homework and investigated Coe's prof-it possibilities by talking to some of its customers and by having some of his friends do so as well. He found that there was a mar-ket for a well made veneer dryer that was backed up by a rep-utable supplier who could provide reasonable services. While Milbourn was not familiar with technical knowledge in the dry-ing field, he did have the necessary management skills, experi-ence and financial acumen. It took some real soul-searching to put everything he had on the line, assume a large mortgage from Central National Bank of Cleveland, and move his Mississippi-born wife and seven-year-old son up to "Yankee Country." What Milbourn got besides a bundle of debts was a decrepit factory, some worn-out machine tools, a Civil War-style foundry and a few knowledgeable employees from the old Coe Company. No one by the name of Coe survived the transition.

Initially, Milbourn thought that he might be the proverbial "one-man band," serving as engineer, salesman and general manager. He did bring in some new people from Tennessee, but he soon found that there was sufficient demand for Coe's prod-ucts that he could not perform all functions. Therefore, he began thinking about who could be of most help to him. That man was his college friend, Arthur Vance, who had been the brightest engineer in the University of Kentucky Class of 1899 and who had a splendid job as manager of the Cincinnati office of the B. F. Sturtevant Company, America's leading manufacturer of fans, heaters and other air handling equipment. Much to Milbourn's surprise and delight, Vance agreed to give up his job and join his old college friend in the bold new venture.

Arthur Vance was just what the new company needed. He had engineering knowledge, he was an accomplished salesman and he knew how to keep records and manage procedures in a grow-ing engineering and sales organization. His admiration for his old college chum increased day by day as he watched Milbourn "wheel and deal," borrow and pay back and basically display genuine American style entrepreneurialship. The two men complemented each other and Coe prospered rapidly. In those days, the income tax was minuscule, so if a company made money, it could be kept! Another important aspect was that all old debts were paid one hundred cents on the dollar, and this resulted in the company being rated "AA" by Dun & Bradstreet. Vance stayed with Coe until a heart condition forced his early retirement in 1937. His contribution was tremendous not only because of his skills, but because of the young men he brought to Coe and trained in his own image. Prominent among these were R. D. "Dick" Moore, Ohio State, 1923, and E. P. "Pat" Morris, University of Kentucky, 1926, both of whom became vice presidents of Coe. Another trainee was Frank W. Milbourn, Sr.'s son, Frank W. Milbourn, Jr., a Princeton grad, class of 1934, who benefited from three years of experience under Arthur Vance's guidance.

Other strong men came with the company in the 1920s. Frederick Krag, an engineering graduate of M.I.T., had been with the "old" company but lost all faith in Coe. His faith was restored and he rejoined Coe when Milbourn and Vance visited him in New York in 1922. He established the New York office to handle strictly eastern board dryer sales. Krag was a truly accomplished gentleman/engineer, having excellent rapport with the top echelon of customer management. In a relatively short time, he became a Coe vice president. He served Coe until he passed away in 1963.

Herbert Masters was another University of Kentucky engineer. He came with the company in 1923 and worked out of his Chicago office handling board dryer and occasionally veneer dryer sales. Masters was intelligent, efficient and, at times, arrogant. He made excellent sales contacts with certain large customers and potential customers. In Krag and Masters, Coe had two heavyweights covering the expanding board industry.

James Rice was an old friend of Arthur Vance. Starting about 1925, he sold the Coe veneer machinery line in the southern states. W. Ross Teachout was a salesman with the old Southern Engine and Boiler Works, and Milbourn brought him along to sell in the Central South. R. H. Plummer, a San Franciscan, was recruited to handle the company's veneer machinery line on the West Coast. The potentially huge Douglas fir plywood industry was in its infancy in 1924 in Washington and Oregon. Arthur M. Conway replaced Plummer in 1927. Conway was experienced in sawmill machinery sales. He was a native of Pennsylvania but moved to the West and never looked back. His office was in Portland, Oregon. All of these men were talented and experienced. All of them sold Coe products exclusively; that is, they represented no company other than Coe.

About 1922, having "learned the ropes" in this new field domestically, Milbourn and Vance decided they should explore the export field. A man named Edward Watts was presumed to be representing the company in export, but no orders were received. Milbourn got one of his experienced Southern Engine salesmen, Neal Journigen, to go with him to New York. The purpose was to simply touch base with Watts and then send Journigen on an exploratory sales mission to Europe. Watts thought he still had certain contract rights to sell Coe machinery abroad, and he thought he saw a new spirit within the revitalized Coe organization. A red-headed Brooklynite, Watts stood his ground; namely, that Watts' company, United States Machinery Company, still had contractual rights to sell Coe machines for export. After several days of discussion, United States Machinery and Coe agreed to split the expenses of the Journigen trip to Europe. Journigen came home six weeks later with orders for two lathes. After that, United States Machinery, and subsequently the United States Wallboard Machinery Company, very successfully handled all Coe export sales (except for Canada) for over fifty years. After Watts passed away in 1960, Coe purchased the United States Machinery Company in 1974 and moved the personnel to Painesville.

In 1920, Coe's product line consisted of veneer lathes, veneer clippers, knife grinders, veneer dryers, and an evolving potential to board dryers. With the exception of the period from mid 1921 to mid 1922 (which marked a short depression), the company during the decade of the 20s made some one-hundred "double-letter" veneer lathes and fifty veneer dryers. The line of double-letter (DD, EE, FF) lathes and their predecessors, the single letter (D, E, F) lathes, were state-of-the-art in their time. By later standards, they were sturdy but slow, requiring considerable maintenance and setup time. But these lathes produced high grade veneer as fast as it could be handled in conjunction with the processing equipment available. Many lathes were driven with steam engines, for in many remote plant locations no electricity was available. The art of motor controls had not advanced and available equipment was expensive and difficult to maintain.

Coe Company tried its hand at revolutionizing the lathe industry in 1923. One of its engineers, Cap Collier, designed the "Twentieth Century" lathe, one which would "render all others obsolete." But the great new lathe was too complex for its operators, resulting in many maintenance problems. After two or three of these machines were installed, the new design was declared a failure. This was a serious financial blow to the Coe Company.

The "double-letter" lathe line was still the best available until about 1933, at which time nobody wanted to or could afford to buy a veneer lathe or any kind of capital goods equipment because of the Great Depression. The operation of the lathe, combined with the off-bearing group and the clipper station, was very labor-intensive. Sixty log turns per minute was considered "highballing." Production of veneer and plywood was becoming an expensive proposition labor wise, but still the timber was available, plentiful and cheap.

As to the Coe veneer dryer, its 1920 model was a multiple deck conveyor dryer consisting of four-inch diameter steel driven rolls on which were mounted sprockets that were chain driven. "Floating" top rolls flattened the veneer as it moved through the dryer. Around this conveyor system was, in effect, an insulated box that channeled relatively slow-moving air. By this time, Coe had established an outstanding name for itself in the field of veneer drying. Arthur Vance and others could see much room for improvement and design resulting in the development of the Model 23 dryer, which used the properties of flash steam and greater air flow, resulting in a new uplift in veneer drying efficiency. Seventy-five of these dryers were installed with about a dozen of them going to the states of Washington and Oregon.

In 1928, the company introduced a vastly improved machine which embodied a much higher velocity air stream, larger fans and heaters along with many other mechanical improvements that were the result of experience with the Model 23 machine. Approximately one-hundred of these machines were installed in the U.S. and in various other countries throughout the world.

Tremendous progress was made in the 1920s in the design and manufacture of board dryers. Waste wood fiber and bagasse (sugar cane fiber) were the ingredients of most fiberboards, although various other refuse materials were tried. These boards were used for sheathing and insulation. Gypsum wallboard (Plaster of Paris between two pieces of heavy paper or light cardboard) found a prominent niche in the building industry. Coe was truly the pioneer in the development of fiberboard and plasterboard dryers including collaborations with Carl Muench of Insulite (International Falls, Minnesota), Bhor Dahlberg of Celotex (New Orleans, Louisiana) and Melvin Baker of National Gypsum (Buffalo, New York). Handling the products into the dryer and taking them away from the dryer involved material handling skills in which Coe was also to become proficient.

In the 1920s all of the well known man-made board products in the United States, and most of those throughout the world, were produced using Coe dryers. Some of the old trademark names were Insulite, Celotex, Insaboard, Ten-Test, Beaver Board, Gypsolite, Maizewood, Certainteed, Maftex and White Rock. Indeed, the business of converting a waste-fiber product into a salable insulation board caused so much worldwide attention that a laboratory was built in Springfield, Ohio, where a board manufacturer could send material to be run on an experimental basis to see if his waste product could commercially be made into a useful product. The laboratory was jointly owned by Coe and three other firms whose equipment was necessary to produce and test potential products. The laboratory was normally rented on a daily basis. Coe and the other suppliers furnished the necessary engineering and staff assistance. Many of the prospective clients were from foreign lands.

While most of Coe's board dryer sales were made to well established companies because of the substantial capital expense involved, many of its veneer lathe and dryer sales were made to companies that were individually owned and operated. In those days, frequently the person ordering the machinery was the one who paid the bills, and the one who personally had to be satisfied with the machinery. In the late 1920s, Coe had become sufficiently prosperous so that it could finance veneer machinery sales on very flexible terms without resorting to bank participation. Many of the terms granted would have looked highly irregular to a banker. But the veneer business was good, and if a veneer plant was well operated, it was truthfully said that the Coe machinery would pay for itself and make a handsome profit for its owner. Of course, timber raw materials had to be available. Credit was usually granted because of a prior acquaintance with the buyer and Coe's judgment as to his integrity and ability.

Another aspect of the growing business was the Field Service Department. In order to ensure that both veneer and board dryers were properly assembled and put in satisfactory operation, a cadre of trained "erectors" had to be developed. All dryers were shipped "knocked down." That is, steel, rolls, sheet metal, fans, castings, chain, etc. were shipped in bulk and had to be assembled in accord with the engineering drawings that had been prepared for the purpose. A certain amount of field fabrication was always required and some modification of parts was necessary to ensure a proper fit. Components like "drive rigs" were completely factory assembled and tested but there was no way that a machine one-hundred feet or more in length with thousands of individual parts could be preassembled prior to shipment.

Mr. Milbourn, Sr. first called upon older experienced servicemen to provide this type of assistance, but soon younger men, usually with engineering training, were recruited. In addition to knowing the design and operation of the dryer involved, the Coe erectors were required to supervise the labor, skilled and unskilled, provided by the customer or outside contractors as the case might be. Needless to say, this was a skill not taught in colleges but had to be acquired—at times the hard way. Most individuals who subsequently became company executives experienced at least to some degree this field service training. It provided an invaluable contact and appreciation of customer problems and new friendships were thus established that proved to be of value to all concerned. Coe was fortunate in having a strong Engineering Department with excellent leadership. This resource was absolutely essential to the success of a machinery building company in Coe's competitive marketplace.

So Coe finished the 1920s in a blaze of glory, emerging from the depth of despair in 1920 to the unqualified leader in its field. The five years, 1925-29, were extremely successful. The place was literally bursting at the seams and more space was needed. Still being primarily engineering oriented, it was decided to build a new office building with good facilities for engineering, sales, purchasing, financial control and management. No one knew that the devastating Great Depression lie just ahead. The stock market crash of 1929 was an indication of the dark clouds on the economic horizon, and then the storm hit.

CHAPTER SIX

THE HISTORY OF COE
(PART THREE)

In 1930, a young Atlantian named Bobby Jones won what was then described as the grand slam of golf. But little else good occurred. From 1930 to 1934, the United States lapsed into a deep, almost indescribable depression. In 1932 the wheels of industry came as close to a complete halt as they had ever come. The task for Coe, and for all companies, was simply to stay alive, keep all necessary talented people on the payroll, and hope for the best.

In 1930, Coe finished its new office building. In the ensuing four years it was the best place in the world to "loaf." There was little else to do. Most orders for Coe machinery in the 1920s were in the $30,000 range. It became obvious during the Great Depression that none of Coe's regular customers was able to spend this kind of money. These customers could not sell their products, hence they were not looking for means of increasing their output. It simply was not economically possible to do so.

So Coe tried to find an item in the thirty dollar range, which it could make and sell with reasonable profitability. After considerable searching it came upon a steam trap with no moving parts. A steam trap is a device that is used to drain the condensate (steam that has turned into hot water) from a heating device. There were thousands of applications for such a device, many of them being employed in some kind of drying medium, such as paper dryers, mangles and shirt dryers in laundries, pulp dryers, chemical dryers and many more, including veneer dryers. In addition, there was the field of process cooking where thousands of steam traps were required. A San Franciscan by the name of Roger Chevalier had for some years been making steam traps with no moving parts for the United States Navy. Because of the roll of a ship, mechanical devices were vulnerable to malfunctioning, so a steam trap with no moving parts was particularly attractive. Chevalier was a bearded, inventive genius. He definitely was not a businessman, and he was annoyed by the hurly-burly of the marketplace.

It is not exactly clear how Coe's Dick Moore and Herb Masters came to meet Chevalier in 1931, but meet him they did. The principle on which Chevalier's device worked was fascinating to Moore and Masters, and after considerable testing and negotiating, it was decided that Coe would design and manufacture for the general industry a commercial version of the device which Chevalier had been supplying to the United States Navy. The idea of attaching a gage glass to the device was Moore's brainstorm. By watching the gage glass an operator could tell if the trap was working properly. Coe would make and market this remarkable new device that was named the "Coe Drainator." The Drainator would be made in various sizes, but the most popular size would sell for about thirty dollars. To make the Drainator would require a gray iron foundry, a shop of medium sized machine tools and assembly benches, all of which Coe had. Naturally, Drainators were supplied on all Coe dryers.

Marketing this product would not be like anything Coe had

ever done before. It was necessary to set up a nationwide network of distributors. Direct mail and vigorous advertising campaigns were started in several trade journals with nationwide distribution. Veteran Coe employees guided this effort. There was little else for them to do.

Gradually, the Drainator business did pick up but it required constant vigilance. Competition from well established steam trap manufacturers was naturally very keen, so the Drainator business was just plugging along until World War II, when suddenly the Navy models became in great demand because of the number of new ships being built. Coe received several million-dollar orders for Drainators. During the "hey days" of the Drainator business, the guiding light was Charles W. "Chick" St. Clair, a widely respected man in the field. He was perfect for the job, having been involved in selling competitive steam traps before coming to Coe in 1936. He not only knew the business, but made friends easily, set up appropriate exhibits at trade shows, and often concluded sales meetings with group singing whenever there was a piano available. After the war, the Navy business lapsed into the doldrums and the regular line of machinery was demanding full attention, and eventually Coe sold the Drainator business and patent rights.

Meanwhile Coe's regular business, i.e., lathes, clippers, dryers, was returning to normal volume in the last half of the 1930s. Customers were still somewhat reluctant to buy new machinery because so many people were remembering the severity of the Great Depression, but confidence was gradually being restored. Major plywood plant expansion was taking place in the Pacific Northwest where complete new Douglas fir plywood plants were installed by M & M Woodworking of Portland, Oregon; West Coast Plywood Corporation of Hoquiam, Washington; Smith Wood Products of Coquille, Oregon; Northwest Door Company of Tacoma, Washington; and Pacific Plywood Company of Willamina, Oregon. All of these plants were completely equipped with Coe lathes, clippers and dryers. There was also production expansion in various other existing Pacific Northwest plants so that the total Douglas fir plywood production in the 1930s tripled from 300 million square feet on a 3/8 inch basis to approximately a billion square feet.

Coe designed and built two new phenomenally good machines in the 1930s. In 1933 it built the first veneer lathe that was designed like a machine tool with precisely built interchangeable parts and anti-friction bearings throughout. It took six years to sell the first one of these because of general business conditions and the skepticism of the new machine. This machine, the Model 233 lathe, was the first giant step forward toward modern, high-production plywood plants. The acceptance of this new design led to the Model 249 and Model 244 lathes, which were larger in size and capable of handling blocks up to ten feet in diameter.

The second phenomenal machine of the 1930s was the Model 330 clipper. For years, sheets of veneer had been clipped by batching two or three or more sheets of veneer for clipping together. This was necessary, otherwise the clipping operation would badly limit the ability of the lathe to produce. Hence, a clipper that would allow rapid single-ply clipping was needed, especially in the Douglas fir industry.

T. R. Robinson was president and founder of Robinson Manufacturing Company of Everett, Washington, one of the early plywood producers. He also had a flair for invention. For many years he had tried to make a single-ply clipper, and he was struggling along when Dick Moore and Art Conway, Coe's West Coast representative, entered the picture. Coe and Robinson agreed to work on the problem together, with Robinson owning the patent and with Coe paying him a royalty of $1,000 per machine. Many years and many thousands of dollars later, Coe perfected and marketed the Model 330 single-ply clipper. It was the "state-of-the-art" clipper in plywood manufacture for almost twenty-five years, even though it was an expensive machine to build and maintenance was substantial because of its many precision parts. Both the anti-friction bearing lathe and the Model 330 clipper were designed essentially by George Haumann, with assistance from his associates in the Engineering Department.

Another great innovation of lasting significance was the gas fired, direct heat board dryer. The first of these made commercially was for National Gypsum Company at Fort Dodge, Iowa in 1937. The product to be dried was gypsum wallboard. Much higher temperatures (as high as 600° F) could be obtained than was available in a conventional steam heated dryer, hence drying times and dryer length were reduced. Good, reliable temperature controls and safety features (against explosion) were required, but they were incorporated through good engineering.

It was only a year later that Coe installed the first gas fired direct heat dryer for drying fiberboard, again for National Gypsum Company. The installation was at National's fiberboard plant in Mobile, Alabama. In order to prevent fires, dryer cleanliness was necessary, but vacuum cleaning devices were installed and the problem was solved. The dryer was an outstanding success. In those days, large quantities of cheap gas were available at all locations. As the construction of gas pipe lines spread across the continent, additional gas fired dryers were installed, many of them being used in the plywood industry.

In the late 1930s other large board dryer installations were made for Johns-Manville Corporation in Jarratt, Virginia and the Ford Motor Company in Dearborn, Michigan. These, however, were steam-heated machines. The Ford dryer was to dry the heavy paperboard backing that goes behind the upholstery in the interior of automobile bodies. National Gypsum Company continued its expansion with two more plasterboard plants and Coe dryers were again selected for each.

Prominent among new personnel at Coe in the 1930s were Arthur S. Holden, who came in 1937 after graduating from Case in 1935 and having spent two years with the Hoover Company. As vice president of the company, Holden gave many years of dedicated service and performed primarily in the sales field. By coincidence, he knew Frank Milbourn, Jr. before coming to Coe, but never anticipated the long association of 50 years that developed.

Another long-time Coe employee who deserves mention is Grover Thornton, whose name became synonymous with field service activities. He came to Coe from Tennessee with Mr. Milbourn, Sr. Grover was a bachelor and hence had no family restrictions that impeded his availability to travel on assignments to all parts of this country and elsewhere in the world. He was an extremely conscientious workman who tolerated no variation from engineering drawings or proper procedures. Many a startled mechanic heard Grover say, "Give me those tools. Get out of my way. I'll do it myself." Mr. Milbourn, Sr. had great respect for Grover and always endeavored to schedule young engineers on a job with Grover to ensure that they learned some "practical science" on top of their degree.

All in all, the 1930s were progressive and profitable years for The Coe Manufacturing Company. But a world war of gigantic proportions lie ahead.

CHAPTER SEVEN

THE HISTORY OF COE
(PART FOUR)

World War II dominated the 1940s but there were also important things that occurred at Coe. In 1940 Coe acquired the area known as the "old mill" property. This included four acres with 500 feet of railroad right-of-way. The property was located directly across Bank Street from the existing operations. It included several old buildings that could be used for storage purposes. This marked the first property acquisition of the "new" management that had come into control in 1920. No one in 1940 could possibly have foreseen how valuable this property would become.

Also in 1940 the first labor contract was entered into following an NLRB election. The bargaining unit chose by a slim majority to represent them was the International Association of Machinists, an American Federation of Labor affiliate. The contract called for an open shop, which the management considered to be a most important provision. There was little fanfare during all these new happenings and at no time was there a work stoppage.

Another 1940 development was the financing by Coe for all of the production machinery in the new Peninsula Plywood plant in Port Angeles, Washington. This was a cooperative style owner-ship plant, and its principals were well known to the Coe man-agement through their involvement in other successful plants. Coe had previously financed the purchase of equipment of its own manufacture in several "co-op" plants under contract terms calling for some forty percent of the purchase price by time of shipment and the balance to be paid over an eighteen-month period. In the case of Peninsula Plywood, Coe, for the first time, purchased machines from other manufacturers and then resold these machines as well as its own under the same terms. By this time, Coe president Frank W. Milbourn had taken on a part-time, non-paying job as president of the First National Bank of Painesville. The banking experience thus gained was helpful in addressing financial problems encountered in the machinery business.

Springfield Plywood, a subsidiary of Washington Veneer, was also built in 1940. The machinery supplied constituted the largest plywood equipment order Coe had ever received. At the same time, Coe put in the first dryer sold in the Wisconsin hardwood industry to Penokee Veneer Company. Compared to Springfield, Penokee was a midget, but the installation was significant. Hard-wood veneers and plywood soon were in great demand in both the United States and Canada as part of the war effort. Other very large integrated plywood plants were subsequently installed by U.S. Plywood at Orangeburg, South Carolina and Plywood Plas-tics Corporation at Hampton, South Carolina. These plants were West Coast style plants that made stock panels from hardwood species, an unusual venture for the Southeast.

As everyone knows, the U.S. declared war on December 8, 1941, but it was quite some time after that before its impact was felt by industrial America, including Coe. Not being a maker of primary war material, Coe continued doing a prosperous business during most of 1942 because many customers were granted priorities to purchase machinery to replace or expand their operations. There was increasing demand for plywood containers for shipping purposes and hardwood veneers and plywood for making aircraft propellers, troop carrying plywood gliders, PT boats and the Mosquito bomber developed by the British. Simultaneously, Coe expended considerable time and effort in developing processes for drying synthetic and guayule rubbers. When the axis nations shut off the U.S. rubber supply, the manufacture of synthetic rubber became a top priority item.

Coe first worked closely with the B. F. Goodrich Company in the manufacture and drying of synthetic. Goodrich developed a process involving forming the synthetic rubber in sheets four feet wide on a fourdrinier machine. Coe designed a conveyor type dryer for drying the product and Goodrich installed eight of them in its Louisville, Kentucky plant.

Because of the urgency of the situation, the country simply couldn't wait to see how the Goodrich sheet process would turn out. William Jeffers, the appointed "rubber czar," decided the producers should "go all out" immediately by making this product by the so-called "crumb" process. No doubt it was a wise decision because efforts of all rubber companies and all dryer manufacturers were put on the same track. It was a known, though little used, process. Coe was called upon to make eight crumb rubber dryers in accordance with a design originated by the makers of dryers primarily used in the textile industry— namely Proctor of Philadelphia, Pennsylvania, and Sargent of Granitville, Vermont. The dryers were installed in groups of four, with one machine always being down for cleaning while the other three were operating. This was necessary because the crumb style synthetic rubber stuck so readily to the chromium plated steel conveyor. But regardless of this stickiness problem, the nation produced the much needed rubber product.

While Coe was making rubber dryers as well as its regular line of plywood machinery, it was called upon by the Cleveland Ordinance District to study the manufacture of a gun mount for a three inch anti-tank gun. Months later, after much study, estimating, soul searching, visiting Washington, D.C. and the Aberdeen Proving Ground, Coe was awarded a prime contract to build 1,667 of the gun mounts for approximately ten million dollars. To do this, a complete rearrangement of the entire factory would be necessary. The "big plan" was that the Cleveland Tractor Company, manufacturer of the vehicle on which the gun mount would be placed, would complete ten such vehicles per day. These vehicles would be given a road test in the form of a thirty-mile round trip to Coe's plant in Painesville, at which point the gun mount would be attached to the vehicle. It sounded like a practical idea.

The Coe organization made an all-out effort to do a good job for the Ordinance Department as its prime contribution to the war effort. It meant a complete change in Coe's way of doing business. But just as a concrete floor was about to be poured in Coe's foundry and all of the machine tools were to be located in a production line mode, word came from the Cleveland Ordinance District that it was canceling the contract for the gun mount. What had happened was that the Cleveland Tractor vehicle had been placed in a race with the other competing vehicles at the Aberdeen Proving Ground. The Cleveland vehicle came in a poor third. This was the reason for canceling the Cleveland Tractor contract and the Coe contract. Coe had not even known there was going to be a race!

Plywood became a strategic product because it was needed for aircraft, shipping containers and for the construction of housing, temporary and permanent, throughout the world. An actual shortage did not develop until late in the war. The war years were not big moneymaking years for Coe, nor should they have been.

One of Coe's war heros was Burt Wilkinson, a member of the 102nd Airborne Division that won the famous Battle of the Bulge. For some thirty years prior to his retirement in 1985, Burt headed Coe's Service Parts Department.

It was not long after V-E Day and V-J Day that the American

economy woke up to the shortages caused by pent up demand during the war. Great demand caused shortages of many materials. Manufacturers such as Coe could obtain no firm deliveries from its suppliers. Virtually every purchase order for materials had to contain a phrase such as "the price to be paid will be the prevailing price at time of shipment."

Once again, a local neighbor provided helpful cooperation in connection with a newly developed lathe, the Model 242. This company was the Harrison Basket Company, located in Painesville. For many years this company had been providing baskets for the fruit-growers in this area, particularly for harvesting and shipping grapes. When the engineering design was completed and the first prototype lathe was built, it was installed in the Harrison plant. There it was possible to observe in operation and identify a few small bugs that needed correction. Frank Harrison, the president, continued to operate the business, which subsequently was moved with other equipment to Walterboro, South Carolina when the company relocated there in early 1953.

Also during the war the next chief engineer was hired from the outside. He was Roy E. Worthington who had previously been in the employ of one of Coe's customers, U.S. Gypsum Company, for almost twenty years. He joined Coe in 1943 and brought with him wallboard machinery expertise and also a sound background of mechanical engineering.

The immediate post-war years were extremely busy ones for Coe. One of the largest plywood plants in the world was installed in French Equatorial Africa by Cia Francais du Gabon, a United States Plywood affiliate. Many other plants enlarged or updated their facilities. Great expansion took place in the plywood industry in the Pacific Northwest, with the Coe Model 244 lathe an instrumental part of it. During the 1940s, large plants were erected in northern California for the first time. New plants started in this period were Humbolt Plywood, Arcata, California; Mutual Plywood, Eureka, California, a hugh co-op; M & M Plywood, Eureka, California; Shasta Plywood, Redding, California; and Calpella Plywood, Calpella, California.

But not all the expansion was in California. Large new plants were built by Mount Baker Plywood, Bellingham, Washington; Southern Oregon Plywood, Grants Pass, Oregon; Umpqua Plywood, Roseburg, Oregon; and Menasha Plywood, Coos Bay, Oregon.

A huge expansion occurred in the board manufacturing field and Coe received many board dryer orders. Simpson Timber Company of Shelton, Washington entered the field and complete new lines were installed by M & O Paper Company, International Falls, Minnesota; Celotex Corporation, Marrero, Louisiana; Armstrong Cork Company, Macon, Georgia; and Johns-Manville, Natchez, Mississippi. Also, Coe's major long-time customer, National Gypsum Company, headquartered in Buffalo, New York, greatly expanded its operations. In addition to installing two new plants, National increased and modernized its facilities at ten other plants. This really was the beginning of automating the loading and unloading of plasterboard dryers. The first basic and detail designs of this came from the inventive brain of Coe engineer, Clarence E. Parker, who came to Coe from the M & O Paper Company in the late 1920s.

Export business thrived. In addition to the plywood plant in Gabon, plywood plants were built in Nigeria, Liberia and French Guiana. Masonite put in a large board plant in South Africa. Coe supplied equipment for new plasterboard plants in Australia, Ireland, Finland and Chile.

The United National Relief and Rehabilitation Authority (UNRRA) purchased three complete plants through Coe's export office for Russia in collaboration with AMTORG, a Russian purchasing entity. Coe's export office, United States Wallboard Machinery Company, seemed to have things under control. Coe had orders for two large plasterboard dryers and one large insulation board dryer. Partial shipments were made and partial payments were received as due. For some unknown reason, all orders were suddenly canceled and it took more than a few days in court in New York to settle things. It must be remembered that the U.S. WWII ally, Russia, was ceasing to be our friend. The

Cold War was "on" and the Iron Curtain had been dropped.

In November 1947, Coe designer and engineer Clarence Parker returned to Painesville from Alexandria, Indiana, where he had superintended the erection of a special dryer in the plant of National Gypsum Company. The dryer was for drying rock wool, a very difficult product to dry. Parker walked into the office of Frank W. Milbourn, Jr., vice president and general manager of Coe, and reported that after a few startup problems, the dryer had been declared a success. Parker also reported that he had become well acquainted with a young man who had been working in the construction crew. He and this young man had frequently gone to lunch and had done a little socializing together. Parker informed Milbourn it was the young man's desire to go to work for Coe. "Well, we will have to get him up here some day," Milbourn, Jr. said. Parker replied, "He just happens to be sitting in our lobby right now." The young man met Milbourn and a few moments later met Coe's president, Frank W. Milbourn, Sr., who hired him as an engineer.

The young engineer's name: Fred W. Fields.

In 1960, I was General Manager of Coe Company's Western Division. We had just moved into the new office and facilities in Tigard, Oregon.

The passing of time may have worked on my physical features, but my enthusiasm for Coe and the wood products business never waned.

My dad, Mahlon Fields, stands second from left, holding one of my siblings. His hard work ethic helped to pull us through the Great Depression. His work ethic and the depression left lasting impressions on me.

My grand-parents, on my mother's side, Will and Lennie Myerly, had a nice farm and were always very helpful to us.

My mother, Ethel, sits at left. Her mom, Lennie Myerly, sits at right. That's my brother, Everett, standing next to my mom, and his son, Jack, beside him (circa 1953).

Yep, that's me sitting on the horse. I began working the fields at our farm at age ten.

Frederic Wilkes and H. H. Coe stand at center with the company's eight employees at the Coe-Wilkes principal building in Painesville, Ohio.

This is the same building that the group photo on the opposite page was taken in front of. Below, middle, aerial of the Coe plant operations in Painesville, after we had added the big press manufacturing facility in the mid 1980s (the big, rectangular white building).

At bottom, Coe Manufacturing offices and plant in Tigard, Oregon shortly after it was built in 1960.

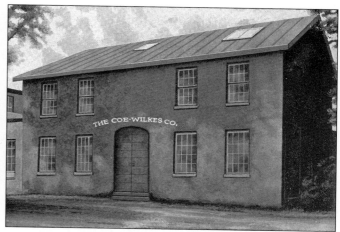

The Coe Engineering Department in action, circa 1948, the year after I started with the company. I'm barely visible at rear left.

In August 1951, owner Frank Milbourn wrote me a letter filled with tremendous encouragement after I had transferred to the Northwest for Coe. The full text of the letter appears beginning on page 81.

THE COE MFG. CO.
INTER-OFFICE CORRESPONDENCE

Painesville, Ohio

August 15, 1951

Mr. F. W. Fields
c/o A. M. Conway
1622 S. E. Sixth Ave.
Portland, 14, Oregon

Dear Fred:

I have your favor of August 12 and I join with you in that we are sorry to have lost the services of George Haumann. As you know, George resigned some time ago - in fact, a month or so ago - and I asked him to come in to Painesville just to talk matters over. He came in and remained several days and by working with him and with Art Conway I thought we had everything straightened out with him, and he promised me to go back to the territory and go to work as usual. This he seems to have done, but very shortly after he got back there he accepted a job with Astoria Plywood and then wrote me that he was resigning, his resignation to take effect August 15, which is today.

When I got this letter I called George and had quite a talk with him but it seems as though I could do nothing with him. He seems to have gotten the idea that some of the dislike him, or that the Conways dislike him - in fact, I could not tell definitely just what was the matter with George - and after doing all I could with him I turned him over to Art Conway. Art talked to him in Portland and found he could do nothing, so all that was left for us to do was to lose his services.

We are sorry to have lost George, but when you can't hold a man you just can't hold him. We could not afford to give him a deed to the property in order to keep him in our services; however, Art Conway offered to do much more for George than I ever thought he would agree to do. I know Art hated to see George leave and I understand that Jim thought likewise.

George is gone, and we are going to miss him some, but if we handle ourselves carefully we will go on and do business at the old stand just as usual. George has left us and that uncovers you to come up and take his place, or better. Right now you are erecting, and if you are not as competent at erecting as George is today as George is, I think you will be in another month or so. I know that George stood well with the presidents and the engineers of the various companies, but if you can go along and get some of our machines running, and will study the business as George ever was. Able to give out advice just as valuable as George was ever able to give out, and the presidents and engineers will look up to you as competent on the West Coast as George ever was.

Sometime it is not too bad for a junior official to have the fellow just above him leave, and likewise sometimes it is not too bad for the company. Consider what has happened in our company in the recent past. Mr. Vance, who was our sales manager, died and thereby uncovered Pat Morris; Dick Moore died and ...

- 2 -

... Holden, Pat and Art are just as good as those they followed. ... and uncovered Howard Price; ... uncovered Norton Oehling. George Haumann has now quit and it ... though Fred Fields has been uncovered.

... really wants you to stay with him, and after you have been ... long to determine that you rather like the West and the ... will be able to make you a proposition which will suit ... would like for you to learn all of our machines, and how ... and then we would like for you to help Conway sell ... know the machines best - or anywhere ... can put up and operate our machines, and if you ... needs and will so advise him, then I think you ... of the buyers, and once you have gained the ... sale ... the machine is about 75% made. I don't ... salesman who has not first learned to put up and ... my thought that you are pretty much on base in ...

... the big lathes on the West Coast and start them ... I think you understand the air clipper and ... understand them better in the early future. ... to ship one of our air clippers to Conway for ... you, and the others, to play with as much as you ... wonderfully proficient on this machine, as ...

... ahead for Coe as hard as you can go; that ... go ahead as hard as you can, I will have ... you get into any trouble at any time and ... and Morris Fox will try to give you some help if you will call and ... of them for a few days to help you understand these lathes very well and ... you will think they can help you out understand the air clipper as well as George ... to get stuck. There may be more work out there to be done at once ... you can do, but I don't think ... do if you have the time to get to it. If there is more work to be done than you ... something to ... I will have to give you some help from here. Again, if you run into ... we within ... do for, for one reason or another, and you will holler to us ... on it.

... of your coming out on top with flying colors if you will ... our machines and their proper application, but how ... job for our customers. In order to be good on our line ... position to advise the customer you must first ... well as our own. When you reach this point they will ... advice rather than to George.

... to say of George, other than he left us with a ... which he was supposed to do. However, I do not

- 3 -

feel too badly over George's leaving as I think it uncovers you and you will be able to fill this job as well as George, and further, that you will be well paid for it. Again we want to admit to you that we have lost a good man in George but when you have a good man that you cannot hold in your employ, then you have to get along without him, and we are determined we are not going out of business because we lose an employee or so.

You must remember that all the time George was going around he was wearing the plume of "chief engineer" for the Coe Company, which did not do him any harm. I think you might as well put this plume on your head as you start out and see if they don't like you as well as, or better than, they did George.

I am going to keep your letter in strict confidence, although I see no reason for doing so, but will do it at your request. The outfit at Portland like you and I think I am due to tell you this, and they would like for you to join them on a permanent basis. You will be talking to Art very soon and if you need me in the discussion I will be glad to get in.

With best regards, we are

Yours very truly,

THE COE MANUFACTURING COMPANY

F.H. Milbourn
President

FWM:s

Everybody seems to be enjoying themselves at the Coe Christmas luncheon in Painesville in 1965. Standing and offering his best holiday wishes is President Frank Milbourn, Jr. Seated left to right are Burt Wilkinson, parts manager; Frank Milbourn III, vice president of manufacturing; Arthur Holden, Jr., vice president of board machinery sales; George Lockman, assistant to the president; and E. P. (Pat) Morris, vice president and sales manager.

Life on the West Coast really wasn't this lonely. We had just moved into the new facilities in Tigard, something I had been pushing for.

ROSEBURG LUMBER CO.

OFFICE · MILL
DILLARD, ORE.

LUMBER · PLYWOOD
P. O. BOX 1088
ROSEBURG, OREGON 97470

TELEPHONE: 679-8741
TWX 503-559-0200

December 4, 1964

Mr. Fred Fields
Coe Manufacturing Co.
7930 S. W. Hunziker Road
Portland 23, Oregon

Dear Fred:

I just finished talking to Frank Spears and during our conversation
he stated that he talked to you a few days ago and that you indicated
the profitability of a Southern Plywood Plant looked very good.

As you know, I had our accountants work up a pro-forma of a
proposed plywood plant in the South. Not that it makes a great
deal of difference, the report which they prepared is not what
you would call lucrative. I am enclosing a copy of this report
and wish you would please go over same and if you find that it
is grossly in error, wish you would please get hold of Dave
Castles and see if we can get the report corrected as I want
to use the report in two or three places soon after the first
of the year.

Very truly yours

ROSEBURG LUMBER CO.

KENNETH W. FORD,
President.

KWF/ew

Enc.

The softwood plywood expansion spread from the Northwest to the Southern U.S. Georgia-Pacific couldn't build southern pine plywood plants fast enough. Coe Company didn't mind at all, as we supplied most of the machinery. In 1964, Kenneth Ford of Oregon-based Roseburg Lumber took a look at southern pine plywood, but backed away.

Model 777 Computerized
Lathe Charger serving
eight foot lathe.

Left hand Positioning
Assembly — Model 777
Lathe Charger.

Here's the "X" and "Why" of it.
Coe's Model 777 Computerized lathe charger.

With soaring timber costs, it's important to attain maximum yield from every block you process. Coe's Model 777 Lathe Charger accomplishes this objective. The 777 provides necessary independent adjustments at both ends of the log so that the maximum diameter of available solid wood cylinder is obtained. Results: Greater full sheet production with minimum strip stock. You can expect 3-5% greater veneer yield, and 10-15% more in full sheets.

The first Model 777 has been in continuous operation since 1977 at Potlatch Forest Products, Lewiston, Idaho, and a second unit was installed there in 1978. Other prominent plywood manufacturers have ordered or are in the process of ordering this equipment.

Here's how Coe's Model 777 Lathe Charger puts the X-Y principle to work. First, in one revolution, it computer analyzes each block at 120 points around its circumference and length. In micro-seconds, this information is fed into the computer, instantly determining the ideal axis of the block. Then the computer instructs the charger to adjust the position of the block — at both ends (the X-Y principle) — to assure that the maximum diameter of solid wood cylinder results when the block is placed in the lathe. A print-out of the number of blocks per shift, log scale per block, computer calculated diameter, and individual log yield improvement is available.

So, learn the X and Why to better log utilization with Coe's 777 Lathe Charger.

The Coe Manufacturing Company • Painesville, Ohio • Portland, Oregon • Atlanta, Georgia

Export Office — U.S. Machinery Division, New York, New York

For more product information, fill out Reader Information Coupon on page 34

Coe's computerized X-Y lathe charger provided tremendous veneer recovery that most companies couldn't pass up. This advertisement appeared in the February 1979 issue of Plywood & Panel World magazine.

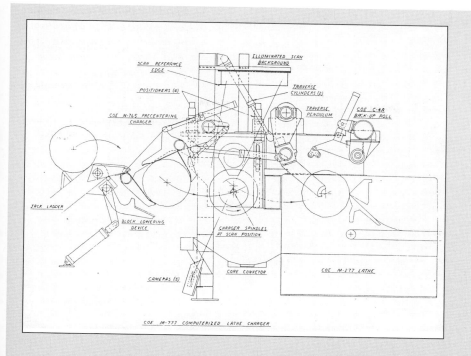

At first, the computerized X-Y late charger featured blocked light, camera scanning, as shown in the above drawing, but later it incorporated the more efficient laser scanning, below, as invented by a brilliant individual named John Nosler.

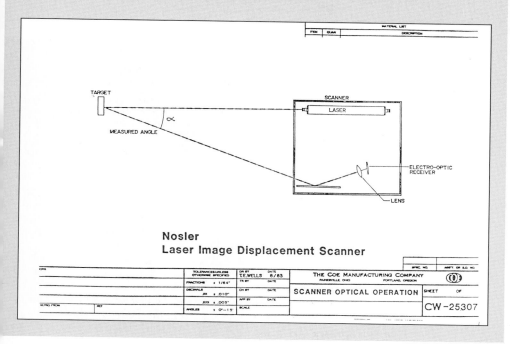

Nosler
Laser Image Displacement Scanner

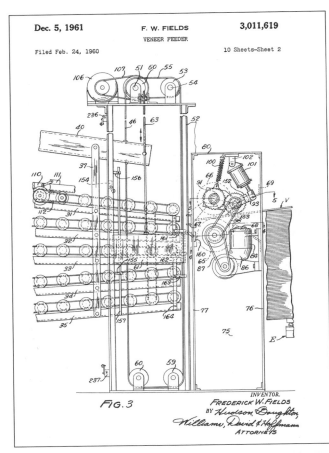

FIG.3

INVENTOR.
FREDERICK W. FIELDS
BY Hudson, Boughton,
Williams, David & Hoffmann
ATTORNEYS

I had the patent on the veneer feeder that was in operation at many plywood mills. We spent a lot of time and money on patents and sometimes I wondered if it was worth the exercise. But I also knew that as soon as we didn't have one is when we would get burned.

Working in the field was part of the job description at Coe from the moment I hired on. Through the years I continued to do my share of plant duty. Here I share a laugh with Bill Bruner of Weyerhaeuser Co. in Hot Springs, Arkansas.

It came about rather unexpectedly, but by the end of 1976 I was the new owner of Coe Manufacturing.

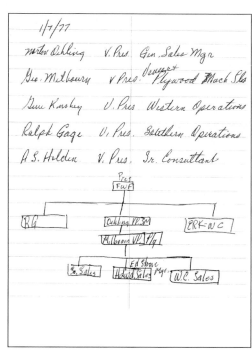

During my tenure as owner and president I filled hundreds of Padmaster shorthand books with my notes. Early in 1977, as the new owner, I was focusing on cash balances and the management team.

Frank Milbourn, Jr.

John Elorriga

Kenneth Ford

Jens Jorgensen (at center)

Leonard Nystrom

The editor and publisher of this book asked me to name ten people in the industry who had tremendous influence on my career. After much soul searching, I came up with the ten men shown on these two pages. Beginning on page 191, I do some reminiscing on each.

Gene Brewer

Bill Hunt

Harold Erickson

Gene Knokey

Art McGee

"Spiraling log costs demand maximum log recovery."

Fred Fields

President
The Coe Manufacturing Company

COE'S ADVANCED TECHNOLOGY PROVIDES YOU
WITH THE TOOLS FOR MAXIMUM PROFITS

Computerized Lathe Chargers — Model 777
develops optimum peel axis for maximum gross recovery.

Veneer Lathes — Model 277
with Hi-speed spindles, digital carriage drives and programmable logic controls provide accuracy and speed required for efficient small log utilization.

Green Veneer Stitchers — Model 1100
develops wide sheets from strips, salvaging veneer that would otherwise be converted into chips.

Hot Melt Unitizers — Model 1200
for assembling dry strip veneer into full size sheets for manual or automatic layup.

R & D AT COE IS WORKING FOR YOU <u>EVERY</u> DAY

The Coe Manufacturing Company • Painesville, Ohio • Portland, Oregon • Atlanta, Georgia
Export Office - U.S. Machinery Division, New York, New York

(Advertisement in Plywood & Panel World magazine, September 1979)

CHAPTER EIGHT

EXPERIENCE IN THE FIELD

So as you can see, before my arrival, The Coe Manufacturing Company had already experienced a history that many manufacturing companies would die for. Personally, I was hungry and I needed a job, and it was a job that paid fairly well. I had no particular preference to which industry I might become involved in. I had decided that when I went to work for Coe, it wouldn't be the end of the world if I didn't like it. I could turn around and go back and finish school. But once I became involved in it I found I liked it very much. The people I became associated with were very first class people and very nice to me in almost every way. I had learned to work hard on the farm, so working hard was not a necessary thing for me to become accustomed to. As long as I liked what I was doing and was reasonably well paid, I had few if any reasons to complain. I moved into a boarding house in Painesville and went to work.

The Milbourns were wonderful people. Mr. Milbourn, Sr. was

a graduate of the University of Kentucky and he had bought the company in 1919, and he was still living and very much in charge when I went to work for Coe. His son, Frank, Jr., was the second in command and a graduate of Princeton. They had three or four other very good responsible engineering people on the management team. Plus Frank Jr. had two sons who were still in school at this time. They were just great people, always very nice to me. It was a fairly small company, probably didn't have 150 employees and most of those were machinists, maybe twelve people in the engineering department, three or four of those were draftsmen and the others were engineers of various types, electrical, mechanical, one chemical engineer. I liked being associated with these people.

When I started at Coe, I didn't have much experience other than college, but I did know how to prepare drawings, so I started work on the drawing board in the engineering department. But I didn't stay there long. Coe had a number of projects for which they were building machinery and they had more projects than they had service people to supervise field installations. They had hired two other engineers before me and they were both young, married and with children under the age of one. I believe one of them had gone to Yale, one to Case Western Reserve and myself. So when it came time to wrestle with a problem out in the field and assist with new machines or old machines, they would go to these two young engineers and ask if they could go. Nine times out of ten their wives would say I don't want you to go, who's going to take care of this baby when I have to do something else. So it fell in my lap to go to these various jobs. As a result it kept me on the run, going from one plant to another, and that was the best experience I could ever have. Knowing enough about the machines to solve the problems and make them perform was important, but the other important thing to me was it enabled me to learn the customers' problems, to find ways and means of solving their problems, not just Coe's problems, that related to Coe's machinery. I was able to carry ideas that the customers had back to Coe's office, which helped in many ways. Coe supplied rotary lathes (peeling machines) and roller dryers and also made clippers and knife grinders back then. I enjoyed doing the field work, I was not married and was free to travel so anytime they blew the whistle I was up and running. It wasn't over a month after I joined Coe Company that I went to my first plant in Richford, Vermont, owned by Atlas Plywood Company, where we were installing a new veneer dryer.

In those early years I was going to mostly hardwood veneer plants, and those plants were mainly in New England and the Carolinas and down South, but I also traveled out west to some softwood plywood plants, and went out of the country to Mexico City and even had an unforgettable experience at a plant in Africa. For about three and a half years, from 1947 to 1951, I was in possibly as many as seventeen plants, all peeling and drying veneer for different types of veneer and plywood products. These plants included Atlas Plywood, Richford, Vermont; Thompson and Swain Plywood, Tuscaloosa, Alabama; McClain Veneer, West Memphis, Arkansas; McCann Lumber, Folkston, Georgia; General Plywood, Savannah, Georgia; Roddis Kraft, Sault Ste. Marie, Ontario; Grand Rapids Veneer, Grand Rapids, Minnesota; Owens Illinois Plywood, Hancock, Vermont; American Seating Company, Lowville, New York; Cheraw Veneer, Cheraw, South Carolina; Menasha Corp., North Bend, Oregon; Southern Oregon Plywood, Grants Pass, Oregon; M.B. King and Company, Amherst, Virginia; Olympia Veneer, Olympia, Washington; Jolin Veneer, Shawno, Wisconsin; Chapas Y Triplay, Mexico City; Acme Tea Chest, Nysaland, Africa. I was really moving around at a fast pace.

Coe continued to treat me very well. When I went on a job for a month or six weeks, Mr. Milbourn, Sr. would ask his son, junior, to get that young fella for lunch and we can see what he learned. We always went to the same place, the Parmly Hotel. I think the first or second time I went to lunch with him, he ordered a steak sandwich and the waitress brought the sandwich, and he tried to cut it but it wasn't very tender and he called the waitress and said, "Young lady, there's nothing that makes a steak any more tender than a good sharp knife. Would you bring me a good sharp knife?" He was a subtle but clever gent. He always took the time to quiz me about anything I had learned about the customer or the equipment. He had gone to the University of Kentucky and worked most of his life at Southern Engine and Boiler Works in Tennessee, but he had a cousin who was a supreme court judge in Mississippi. Mr. Milbourn used to talk about salesmen and how to go about selling machinery, and he'd say, "Well, Judge Ethridge made a ruling one time that a salesman could exaggerate as much as forty percent. And that's in the court records in Jackson, Mississippi."

Frank Milbourn, Jr. always made a point to take me out to dinner along with his wife and we always had a good long talk. They became about as near to family as I could get. They were terrific. When I went out on a job I was pretty much on my own and being in that position I had a tendency to be a little more careful, more responsible because I wanted to see that the company got credit for a job well done. I never had a complaint from anyone.

My first job was to install a roller veneer dryer at a plant owned by Atlas Plywood Company in Richford, Vermont, on the Canadian border. They peeled birch veneer, low grade that went into making those old plywood crates for shipping refrigerators, stoves and other household appliances. Plants of this kind were not very sophisticated technology back then and the people working in the plants were not all that well educated, and when I found someone who knew something, I sort of hung out with him and tried to learn something. I often found people who were without an education but had years and years of experience working with this type of material and they were darn good sources of information.

In my early years I went to Tuscaloosa, Alabama to work with Thompson and Swain Plywood Company. Louise Thompson ran the business and Mose Swain was the log procurer and ran the mill. He had been a great lineman at the University of Alabama in the early 1930s, and had played for head coach Frank Thomas. Mrs. Thompson treated me like I was a little child. She took me to university plays and musicals, and always had me busy doing something. She was an older lady but she was bright and a perfect southerner. They made veneer for other custom manufacturers, such as drawer bottoms and various types of veneer and plywood products

I went to General Plywood's plant in Savannah, Georgia, where I assisted one of Coe's old pro engineers with the installation of a couple of big dryers. These machines were maybe eighty feet long, twenty-five feet wide, probably twenty feet high. They were in a hurry to build the plant, so they needed two men to supervise the work to make sure everything was done right, and fast. So I assisted Grover Thornton of Coe, who was a crabby old guy. He really was on my case all of the time. If I didn't do things his way he'd let me know about it in a hurry. I had a wonderful education from him. I learned a few tricks from him.

I was able to travel to the Western U.S. for the first time to work at the new Menasha Plywood in North Bend, Oregon. I rode the train and en route I met Jack Fleischer, who was director of the Forest Products Research Society in Madison, Wisconsin. He and I played bridge all the way across the country. We became very good friends over the years. On my second trip I traveled to Olympia Veneer at Olympia, Washington and rebuilt a couple of old dryers. At the time I didn't have a particular desire to go to the Northwest other than it was part of my job. I found the people friendly. I would not have told you then that I had any desire to retire in the West as I did.

I had learned to work hard and be fairly resourceful from the farm and working with antiquated machinery. If something broke down you had to get it back together and get on with the work, there were no excuses. You couldn't say the service man didn't show up. That background certainly helped a great deal those first three or four years when I was sent out and doing field engineering. Sometimes if a dryer was to be put together, with four or five carloads in pieces, none of which had ever been assembled, it took a little bit of ingenuity to put it all together. I could always get on the telephone and say something was mis-manufactured, but this left me to use my own ingenuity in taking care of the problem.

Another memorable trip was to the Chapas Y Triplay plant in Mexico City, where I installed a veneer lathe. I didn't know too much about lathes at the time, but when there's no one else around, one must find a way to succeed and you learn a lot in a hurry. The manager's name was Thorvald Nin and he later became manager of the U.S. Plywood plant in Quesnel, British Columbia. He was a wonderful Mexican fellow, very bright, very talented.

During those early years I even had the experience of combining work with a little bit of football. I mentioned previously that I had played football in high school, and then in college and also while I was in the service. I guess I still had a little bit of football left in me even after I went to work for Coe. A year or so after I joined Coe I was assigned a project in Quebec City, Canada. The company, named J. Ulyss Ste. Marie, was building a hardwood plywood plant. My assignment was to supervise the installation of two lathes, a dryer and miscellaneous other machinery. During that period the owner had formed one of the first football teams in the Canadian football league. I had known about it and being a young and inquisitive guy, I became involved. I finished my work on the job at four o'clock and football practice started at five. Being in the middle of summer, I asked one of the principals if they minded if I worked out with the football team. They said, not at all, come on out. The exercise and practice field was within several blocks from the hotel where I was living so it was easy for me to go home and prepare for football practice. Mind you everyone in that area spoke French and it was difficult for me because they called signals in French and it was a different type of football in that they played twelve man football compared to American football with eleven players. Another major difference was that the halfback or fullback could start running at any time as long as he didn't cross the line of scrimmage before the ball was snapped. This created some major collisions at the line of scrimmage. Anyway I did not go out to become a part of the football team, but to get the exercise. As time went on and the season started, they said we need you, why don't you play with us. I said I don't know if that's kosher because I have a job and I'm working for the boss. Mind you the owner couldn't speak English, and so anytime I wanted to say something to him I had to go through an attorney. The attorney checked with Mr. Ste. Marie and he came back and said that Mr. Ste. Marie said it was quite all right and that they would take care of any difficulties that might come up.

I think we had played four or five games when I finished the project. I told the superintendent that I was finishing the following week and I was preparing to go back to Painesville where I was headquartered. And he said but you're playing football and he went to talk to the attorney. The attorney came out to see me the next day at the job site. He said Mr. Ste. Marie wants you to continue on for the rest of the season. I said we've got three or four games to play, I've got to go back to my regular job. He said we'll take care of that, give us your boss's name and we'll call him tomorrow. I said, holy smokes, I've really gotten myself in trouble. I called Mr. Milbourn, Sr. that night and said I've gotten myself in trouble. He said, uh oh, thinking I had gotten myself in trouble with a girl up there. I said oh no, it isn't that, it's just that I've been playing football for Mr. Ste. Marie's team and they have asked that I finish the season, but it's time to come home and continue my work. I told him they're going to call you tomorrow and tell you the details of this and I don't know what you can tell them, but I'm ready to come home, I want my job, I'm not interested in playing football. The next day they called Mr. Milbourn and he was very nice as always and they came to an agreement that if they would pay my expenses and pay my salary while I was up there playing football that Mr. Milbourn would let me stay. So I stayed another four weeks. It was fun. We didn't win the league, I think we finished third. It was the first year that they had Canadian football and some of the playing fields were gravel and broken glass. I played some right half-back and also played right tertiary, which is what we would call right guard in America. I was a pretty husky guy, 6-2, 225, though I wasn't the biggest guy on the team. They had three or four Americans on the team, but the rest of them were French-men and had gone to some of the Canadian colleges. It was an interesting experience and both Mr. Ste. Marie and Coe Compa-ny were very generous in permitting me to play. Back in those days if I had gone from college to play football, a person playing in that position would make 2200 dollars a year. I couldn't afford to do that. I needed to get myself established in a meaningful job. I had the job so I really had to take care of it and continue my education with the company.

Speaking of playing a physical sport such as football, someone once asked me if I had ever gotten into a fight or seen a fight while I was doing field work in those years, the point being that project work could put people under a lot pressure with budgets and deadlines looming, and given the sometimes rough charac-ters that you come across in a mill. But I never got into a fight with anyone. I had a lot of shouting matches I'll say that. I also don't think I ever saw any mill people get in a fight with each other. It got pretty feisty at times. I did threaten a guy once, not his well being, but I was trying to get him to adjust a timer on a tipple. This was on the West Coast and I was only 25 or 26 years old. He didn't want to do it. I knew what I was doing and he was head electrician in the plant. I was operating the lathe and I said to him would you increase the speed of that tipple. He said no I don't think that's the thing to do, we're just starting this up. And I said it needs to be increased and I called to him two or three times and finally I yelled at him with some pretty harsh language that if you don't increase the speed I'll be down there and do it myself. He increased it and walked away. The startup progressed successfully.

CHAPTER NINE

FROM LAID OFF TO AFRICA

Business at Coe overall had been going well since the war. The company's first major building expansion at Painesville occurred in 1948. It was a new 30,000 square foot machine assembly building, which was built on the "old mill" property that had been purchased just before the war. This provided additional assembly space and machine shop space, But about the time I finished in Mexico City, business had dropped off considerably. This was in 1949. I thought I was doing a pretty good job and I had nice compliments from most of the people where I had been working. I had no demerits so to speak. I went back to Painesville from Mexico City and Frank Milbourn, Jr., who was the vice president and son of the owner of the company, said I'm sorry but I'm going to have to lay you off. We just don't have any business. It really broke my heart because I thought I was doing everything they could expect from me, and he verified that I had done everything they could expect from me. But I was laid off and went back home to Indiana. I didn't really think I would be returning to Coe. There was a tough recession going on and I was looking for a job to do, but I had come to know wood products and particularly plywood fairly well and I wanted to stay in the wood business if I could. Fortunately I got a job with Palmer G. Lewis Company in Indianapolis. They were wholesalers for hardwood and softwood plywood, so I was selling plywood to lumber and building material yards. I was really getting into the swing of things and selling plywood like it was spaghetti.

Then after about four months, Frank Milbourn, Jr., wrote me a letter and asked me if I would be interested in taking a job for Coe. It was in east Africa at a plywood plant that was being built to produce tea chests. The plant was to make veneer to be made into these tea chests, which were simply shipping boxes that were sixteen inch squares at bottom and top and maybe twenty-two to twenty-four inches high. They were to line these boxes with aluminum foil and pack them with green tea for shipment to Europe. The company, Acme Tea Chest, was headquartered in Glasgow, Scotland and was in the business of making aluminum foil not only for these tea chests but also for things such as cigarette packages. I had met the people from Scotland in Painesville before I was laid off. I had lunch with the two principals. They got their plant building partly built and it was about a year later that the machinery was assembled and shipped to the plant site and they called Coe and said we need somebody to supervise the installation and the operation and to teach our people how to make these machines perform. So Coe responded that they would send a guy over and these fellas said well we'd like that fella we met when we were in Painesville, we'd like him to come. So Coe wrote me a letter and asked me if I would be interested. Going to Africa was a challenge and experience that I would probably never have again and I decided that even though I had gotten a new job that I really liked, I thought I'll go and do this job and when we finish it I'll have the option of going back to school or taking another job if Coe doesn't want me.

I went to the country of Nysaland in British East Africa, as it was called then, now it's called Milowi. The small town was named Chiciboula, maybe seventy-five miles from the nearest civilization. I spent the better part of six months there. It wasn't the end of the earth, but you could see it from there. We were installing two Coe lathes and a Coe dryer. As you might expect, there were a lot of wild animals around, lions, elephants, and all the people were natives except for three Europeans and I. In those days these natives had never had a job. They didn't know what a job was, all they did was barter. I was given about a hundred of these natives to work with. Usually when I went on a job to put machinery together, by the time I got there the concrete floor was already poured and the foundations ready for you to go to work. I went there and they didn't have the floor poured. Simply they said there's a group of natives for you and they can prepare the ground and pour the concrete. I thought I'll never get through with this. I picked a foreman and he couldn't speak English, none of them could. I called him Pencil Number One and he was my right hand man. He could understand sign language and he could then communicate that to the others. To level the ground for pouring the concrete I would see these little old native men hunched down in their bare feet. They'd have a little board and smooth it out with their hands. You get about forty of them out there and you can get a lot of work done. It was really quite interesting in those primitive conditions.

One thing that happened was as I was putting this machinery together I suddenly realized the factory had assembled the dryer drive incorrectly. A drive mechanism for example has a right hand drive or a left hand drive depending on which side the drive chain is on in the machine. Unfortunately when the shop in Ohio assembled the drive rig—as they're all pre-assembled before they leave the factory—they were shipped right-hand and they should have been shipped left-hand, or vice versa, so I had to cut the chain tightener apart and fabricate and reassemble it in the opposite hand. That was mainly all weldment, prefabricated and welded together. But the drive rig consisted of shafts, gears and bearings and it was bolted together consisting of twenty large gears in the drive mechanism and were all assembled in the opposite hand so we had to take the whole thing apart and reassemble. It wasn't that it was such a mysterious thing to do but with a group of African natives who had never had a job before, let alone become a mechanic, I had to do all the work myself. I had only been with the company a couple of years so some of the equipment I had never even seen before.

I think that was probably the most complicated task I ever had to that point. The only thing I had to work with was a few common tools and these natives who had never worked a day in their lives. They would squat on the ground and chew on a piece of sugar cane and look at this funny looking guy and wonder what is he doing. It was another example of being on your own, being out in the field, and knowing what the project is and what you have to do. There are no projects just like the last one. You take the bull by the horn and see that the job is done properly and as efficiently as possible.

I look back on that experience and it was a lot of fun. They had built three homes for the three European people there. One of them was the general manager, one was the president's son. I lived with the president's son. These were buildings made out of homemade brick and they used asbestos corrugated roofing for the roofs, very heavy material that you wouldn't be caught dead using today. The floor was concrete, and the side walls were homemade brick. They had very fine yellow clay in that part of the world. They would use large ant hills to make a brick kiln.

There was a little store about a mile away run by an old English family. They had been in Africa for a generation or two and there were several of these stores scattered throughout the countryside. They sold liquor and various groceries. The natives didn't eat much of anything. When lunch time came along they didn't have anything to eat. They didn't mind that. They'd bring with them a piece of sugar cane, maybe four or five inches long and they'd take a bite of sugar cane every once in a while.

We were making progress and after about two months the manager from Acme Tea Chest suggested I should go on R and R. I went down to Salsbury in southern Rhodesia and stayed in the Central Hotel and it so happened there were about ten young men there with American Tobacco Company and they were experts in tobacco and one of them was the son of the president of the company. We got along together and they welcomed me into their group and we drank out of the same beer bottle so to speak. We had a really good time for about ten days. Then I went back up to the plant site and we finally got the plant finished and the machinery installed. It wasn't running yet when I left, as the electrical work wasn't done, but I know they eventually got it done and took another six months to finish up and start up the plant.

The day I was leaving, all the natives knew I was leaving and they felt they had to give me a going away present. I arrived down at the plant to say goodbye to them in the morning, and everyone of them brought me an egg. Can you imagine that? They didn't have anything and an egg was about as dear to them as anything. I really appreciated it. Of course I couldn't take all of these eggs with me and when I got out of the natives' sight I gave the eggs to the managers. I was extremely touched. It was one of my fondest memories from my field work with Coe.

Meanwhile we had another engineer over on the west coast of Africa in Gabon, French Equatorial Africa. I left where I was in British East Africa and went half way down the continent, to Johannesburg and Capetown and then went up the west coast to Lepoldville and went to visit this fellow in Gabon. His name was Dick Van Halla and he was with the Coe engineering department and he was doing the same type of thing I was doing, putting up a big plywood plant. This plant was being built with Marshall Plan money for the French government. It was a little bigger plant than the one I was involved in. He had been over there about seven or eight months and when he saw me at the airport I thought he was going to go out of his mind as he was so glad to see anybody who was white and could speak English. I stayed there about ten days and he showed me around and we went to Norwegian whaling stations and had a very interesting stay. After leaving Africa, I visited Acme Tea's home office in Glasgow, Scotland to report on the plant's status; again a very interesting trip and nice visit.

When I had departed for Africa I wasn't sure what my status would be with Coe upon my return, whether I would want to leave or whether Coe would want me to stay. As is turned out I wanted to stay and so did Coe. They treated me so well when I came back from Africa, the economy had turned around and I continued on with Coe.

CHAPTER TEN

GO WEST YOUNG MAN

It wasn't long before I was bound for the Great Northwest, on a permanent basis you might say. I had worked in the West a couple of times for Coe. The people in the plywood plants were pretty much brothers. There were no family secrets. I went to Menasha Plywood and installed two lathes and two dryers, a long job for me, but a very good, productive job. I had met the manager there, Dick Bourn, a very friendly and accommodating guy. Chuck Douce was the president of Menasha Corp. and Jim Cooper was the superintendent and he really helped me a great deal in getting around and knowing some of the things about the West Coast plywood industry. I had visited Columbia Plywood at Kalama, Washington between Portland and Longview. There I had met Gene Knokey's father. Gene was working there with him, just out of high school. Gene would become an instrumental part of the Coe team some years down the road. I went to Southern Oregon Plywood in Grants Pass and installed two lathes and two dryers. There I met Carl Jacobson and Ernie Clark, who were like fathers to me and we just had a wonderful relationship. I also met Jack Beaman, who eventually became president of American Plywood Association. I probably spent three or four months with them. I also spent a great deal of time at U.S. Plywood's plant in Anderson, Calif., where I first met Gene Brewer. They also had a NovaPly particleboard or chip board plant going there so there was a lot of activity and engineering people around.

In those days in the West, Coe had a manufacturer's agent or representative, called A.M. Conway & Son, which was Art Conway and his son, Jim. They were located in Portland and Art Conway had represented Coe since 1927. Coe was their primary representative manufacturer, but they did represent other companies. Rather than Coe carry the burden or expense of a sales organization in the Northwest, and have the expense of people traveling around and entertaining customers, it was in those days customary for a company like Coe to have a manufacturer's representative. Coe had a manufacturer's rep in North Carolina to cover the east, one in Mississippi to cover the South, Art Conway out West and U.S. Machinery Company to handle the international business.

By the time I arrived there, Art Conway was a well known individual throughout the industry and was as successful as those people were in those days. He was up in years when I joined him. You have to remember back in those days during the war and immediately after the war there were probably only ten to fifteen plywood plants located in the Northwest. It was easy to get acquainted with most of the people in the business. After the war, plywood plants started to spring up here and there and in a lot of cases they were cooperatives. Those cooperative plants would ask for a shareholder to invest five thousand dollars and they would get two or three hundred shareholders and raise enough money to build a building. One of the original cooperatives was Peninsula Plywood in Port Angeles, Wash. Mr. Milbourn of Coe financed their purchase of the machinery for that entire plant. Coe did not build all the machinery that was used in a plywood plant, but there were other machinery manufacturers he bought machinery from and installed these in their plant so they got running at a very low cost. Most of the people in the plywood business looked to him for some kind of financing when they bought the machinery.

Art Conway was a very accommodating sort of a fella. He wasn't a character, he wasn't a heavy drinker and he didn't do a lot of heavy entertaining. He was just a nice guy and he knew the machinery business pretty well. It was fairly simple in those days. I'm not trying to make his job a simple one, excepting that's the way things were. A lathe for example was fairly simple, with a steam engine drive on it in most plants. Art Conway was a very important person in that he knew a lot of people in the business and they knew him, and even though he may not have had the technical knowledge about the machinery, he certainly talked the language very well.

When I arrived they had a field engineer, an older man, named George Haumann and he was very bright. But within a year after I arrived Haumann quit or walked out. I wrote Mr. Milbourn, Sr. that I thought it was just a shame to lose a talented guy like George Haumann, and that if there was anything I could do to encourage him to stay on with the company to please let me know. Mr. Milbourn wrote me back a long letter and gave me the inside story on Haumann, and told me not to worry about George, but to put on my cap so to speak and if somebody asks me, to tell them I'm the new chief engineer and I'll fix their problems.

Here's the letter Mr. Milbourn wrote me, dated August 15, 1951:

> Dear Fred,
>
> I have your favor of August 12 and I join with you in that we are sorry to have lost the services of George Haumann. As you know, George resigned some time ago—in fact, a month or so ago—and I asked him to

come in to Painesville just to talk matters over. He came
in and remained several days and by working with him
and with Art Conway I thought we had everything
straightened out with him, and he promised me to go
back to the territory and go to work as usual. This he
seems to have done, but very shortly after he got back
there he accepted a job with Astoria Plywood and then
wrote me that he was resigning, his resignation to take
effect August 15, which is today.

When I got this letter I called George and had quite a
talk with him but it seems as though I could do nothing
with him. He seems to have gotten the idea that some of
us dislike him, or that the Conways dislike him—in fact,
I could not tell definitely just what was the matter with
George—and after doing all I could with him I turned
him over to Art Conway. Art talked to him in Portland
and found he could do nothing, so all that was left for us
to do was to lose his services.

We are sorry to have lost George, but when you can't
hold a man you just can't hold him. We could not afford
to give him a deed to the property in order to keep him in
our services; however, Art Conway offered to do much
more for George than I ever thought he would agree to
do. I know Art hated to see George leave and I understand that Jim thought likewise.

George is gone, and we are going to miss him some,
but if we handle ourselves carefully we will go on and
do business at the old stand just as usual. George has
left us and that uncovers you to come up and take his
place, or better. Right now you are erecting, and if you
are not as competent at erecting our machines today as
George is, I think you will be in another month or so. I
know that George stood well with the presidents and the
engineers of the various companies, but if you can go
along and get some of our machines running, and will
study the business of our customers, you will be able to

give out advice just as valuable as George was ever able to give out, and the presidents and engineers will look up to you the same as they have looked to George for advice in the past. I know that if you are not already in this position, that before the snow flies you will be just as competent on the West Coast as George ever was.

Sometimes it is not too bad for a junior official to have the fellow just above him leave, and likewise sometimes it is not too bad for the company. Consider what has happened in our company in the recent past. Mr. Vance, who was our sales manager, died and thereby uncovered Pat Morris; Dick Moore died and uncovered Art Holden. Pat and Art are just as good as those they followed. J.S. Rice died and uncovered Howard Price; Teachout got in bad physical condition and uncovered Norton Oehling. George Haumann has now quit and it looks to me as though Fred Fields has been uncovered.

Art Conway really wants you to stay with him, and after you have been with him sufficiently long to determine that you rather like the West and the work, I think Conway will be able to make you a proposition which will suit you very nicely. We would like for you to learn all of our machines, and how to put them in operation, and then we would like for you to help Conway sell them. I believe that the best future salesman for the West Coast—or anywhere else—is going to be the man who knows the machines best, and who can put them up and operate them. If you can put up and operate our machines, and if you understand what machines a man needs and will so advise him, then I think you will have gained the confidence of the buyers, and once you have gained the confidence of the buyers the sale of the machine is about 75% made. I don't think we ever want another salesman who has not first learned to put up and operate our machines. It is my thought that you are pretty much on base in this respect already.

I think you can put up the big lathes on the West Coast and start them into production as well as George. I think you understand the air clipper and the 330 clipper very well and will understand them better in the early future. In about two weeks we are going to ship one of our air clippers to Conway for him to put up in his place for you, and the others, to play with as much as you like. By doing so you will become wonderfully proficient on this machine, as well as the dryer and other machines.

You say that you are going ahead for Coe as hard as you can; that is all I want you to say. If you will go ahead as hard as you can, I will have no fear of this outcome. However, if you get into any trouble at any time and cannot manage a machine, we will try to give you some help if you will call on us. I think Claude Oliver and Morris Fox understand these lathes very well and if you should need one of them for a few days to help you out, I will send him over to you. I think they can help you out if you get stuck, but I don't think you are going to get stuck. There may be more work out there to be done at once than you can do, but I don't think there is going to be any work that you can't do if you have the time to get to it. If there is more work to be done than you can get to, we will have to give you some help from here. Again, if you run into something you cannot do, for one reason or another, and you will holler to us we will give you help on it.

I have no doubt of your coming out on top with flying colors if you will arrange to study not only our machines and their proper application, but how they can do an efficient job for our customers. In order to be good on our line of machinery and be in a position to advise the customer properly, you must first understand his business as well as our own. When you reach this point they will all be looking to you for advice rather than to George.

I have nothing unkind to say of George, other than he left us with a world of machinery to put up which he was supposed to do. However, I do not feel too badly over George's leaving as I think it uncovers you and you will be able to fill this job as well as George, and further, that you will be well paid for it. Again we want to admit to you that we have lost a good man in George but when you have a good man that you cannot hold in your employ, then you have to get along without him, and we are determined we are not going out of business because we lose an employee or so.

You must remember that all the time George was going around he was wearing the plume of "chief engineer" for the Coe Company, which did not do him any harm. I think you might as well put this plume on your head as you start out and see if they don't like you as well as, or better than, they did George.

I am going to keep your letter in strict confidence, although I see no reason for doing so, but will do it at your request. The outfit at Portland like you and I think I am due to tell you this, and they would like for you to join them on a permanent basis. You will be talking to Art very soon and if you need me in the discussion I will be glad to get in.

With best regards, we are

Yours very truly,

The Coe Manufacturing Company

F. H. Milbourn

President

You can imagine the world of encouragement this letter gave me that I wouldn't have had otherwise. Of course it also put a lot of responsibility on my shoulders, which I didn't mind one bit. Obviously it was in the works for my association with Conway to become even tighter.

One thing I remember about Mr. Conway was him saying time

and time again, the plywood growth is over and we've got more
plywood plants and production than the world will ever con-
sume. He was always a pessimist. He always thought the plywood plant being built today was going to be the last plywood
plant ever built. He had no confidence unfortunately that the
industry was going to have any growth. His son, Jim, was a very
nice man, and an avid outdoorsman. He had a deep sea tuna fishing boat and he had an airplane and he could fly from Portland to
the coast and go out about twenty-five miles into the ocean, fish
for tuna all day and be home in Portland in time for dinner. I
went hunting and fishing with him a few times, but very rarely.
There may have been plenty of work going on, but when Jim
found that the fish were running and the birds were flying, he
had to go. Anyway Jim just wasn't showing real strong attention
to the plywood business. The production of Douglas fir plywood
in the Pacific Northwest was really exploding and it was important that Coe had somebody in place in the West to handle this
tremendous growth of business.

Mr. Milbourn, Sr., realized they needed some help and he suggested they hire someone, and after a certain period of time Mr.
Conway told Mr. Milbourn he couldn't find anybody. I had
recently been doing field work in the West and had of course
become acquainted with the Conways. I wasn't sitting in the
office with them, I was out in the field, but they knew the people
I was working with and they talked with the customers and got a
feel for my capabilities. Mr. Milbourn said well we've had that
fella Fields out there doing some engineering work, why don't
you make him a proposition. Mr. Conway replied that he didn't
realize Mr. Milbourn and Coe were willing to let me go. Mr.
Milbourn said, I don't want to, but if that's what it takes, we
will. I think Mr. Conway realized I was making myself a little bit
of a reputation out there and he asked me to join him in the business, which I did. And so we formed Conway and Fields in
1951. My responsibilities were about the same, except now I
became more involved in the marketing aspect of the business
while doing field engineering. And of course now I was a partner

in my own business. I felt good about it. Mr. Milbourn was encouraging me to do that. I'd only been with the company a few years and I had let it be known that I enjoyed my work and if other opportunities presented themselves that I'd like to be considered. This happened to be one that required somebody to move and in those days I was not married and I could move at a moment's notice.

When I moved to Portland I had so much work going on for Coe, more work to do than I had time to do it, so I kept traveling and basically living out of the trunk of my car the first couple of years. I remember staying at places like the North Bend Hotel in North Bend, Oregon, the Redding Hotel in Redding, California, the Redwood Hotel in Grant's Pass, Ore. Those old places have all gone by the wayside. You could rent a room for three dollars a night. I'd have as many as five projects going on at a time in various stages. Some of the companies and plants that come to mind were Edward Hines in Oak Ridge, Oregon, Weyerhaeuser in Springfield, Oregon, Norply in Crescent City, California, Standard Veneer and Plywood in Crescent City, Umpqua Plywood in Green, Oregon and Roseburg Lumber in Roseburg, Oregon. I finally rented an apartment in 1955. I didn't mind the hard work. Hard work never seemed to effect me very much. I loved the Northwest and the people. I learned a great deal and I think I taught them a few things. They didn't have engineers on the job; they might have a surveyor, they were master mechanics and mill superintendents and when I went on the job they always were congenial and would take me to lunch or dinner and I might be on the job for two or three months and I became very well acquainted with those individuals and they were the type of people who were more than happy to share their knowledge with me. It was a very pleasant learning experience. Some of those master mechanics were very smart and they might not do everything the way a very technically informed engineer might do it, but they might have a short cut; they were great people to learn from.

In addition to those I just mentioned, in the 1950s new plywood plants using Coe machinery were built by Woodard Lum-

ber Company, Coast Plywood, Simpson Timber, Fruit Growers
Supply, Martin Brothers Box, Multnomah Plywood, MacMillan
Bloedel, Willamette Builders Supply, Canadian Western Lumber,
Mount Baker, Zip-O-Logs, Milwaukee Forest, Fir-Ply, Vancou-
ver Plywood, Durable Plywood, Coos Head Lumber, Union
Lumber, Evans Products, Eureka Plywood, Siskiyou Lumber,
Natron Plywood, Oregon Veneer, Fullerton Lumber, Jefferson
Plywood, Bate Lumber, Long Bell Lumber, Kogap, Port Orford
Plywood, Hult Lumber, SDS Lumber, Dwyer Lumber, Trinity
Alps Lumber, Pope and Talbot, Fort Seward Lumber, Willamette
Valley Lumber, Rochlin Veneer, Winton Lumber, Powers Veneer,
Snellstrom Lumber, Cal-Ore Veneer, Coquille Plywood, Ply-
wood Corporation of America, International Paper, Rosboro
Lumber, Pickering Lumber, Paragon Plywood, Brookings Ply-
wood, Medford Corp., to name more than just a few. Annual pro-
duction from the West skyrocketed from 2.5 billion square feet
on a 3/8 inch basis in 1950 to 7.8 billion in 1959.

That brings to mind a study conducted in the 1950s by Stanford Research Institute for Weyerhaeuser Timber Company. It
was published in 1954 and its purpose was to depict the growth
and demand for all forest products in the United States through
1975. It reported that U.S. softwood plywood production should
reach 7.2 billion square feet by 1975. In reality, in 1975 softwood plywood production was more like 16 billion square feet!
It had already surpassed 7 billion square feet in 1959. The report
hadn't seen the coming of southern pine plywood or the continued growth in the West. Everybody used to joke about that
report. I hope nobody bet the farm on it.

The dominant machine in many of these mills in the 1950s
was the well established Coe Model 244 lathe. A few larger ver-
sions of this same machine were supplied to take larger logs.
These were called Model 247 lathes. I remember some of those
Canadian plywood plants, like Canadian Forest Products,
MacMillan Bloedel, Weldwood of Canada, MB King on the
Frazer River in Burnaby, Crown Zellerbach in New Westminster.
Those were big plants, two and three lathe plants and high pro-

duction. In those days Coe competed in the lathe business with Premier and to some degree with Merritt. I am confident we got at least 60% of the lathe business.

The difference in those days and today was the logs were much larger. The number of revolutions per minute on a lathe was much slower, but the flow of veneer off the lathe was as fast or faster than it is today. Today logs are much smaller logs, with much more defect and no grade in them, no A faces or B backs, it's C and D types of veneer. To get the same volume of veneer from a lathe it has to run at a much higher rate of speed. In the early years when they were peeling the larger logs, oftentimes they would reject the core out at ten or twelve inches in diameter. Today they're kicking core out at two inches in diameter. In the early years sometimes we got a 110 inch diameter log in the lathe, nine feet. We didn't get too many of them. I'd say the average log diameter might have been forty inches. The bigger logs usually had the best grade in them, and the value difference in grade between A and C veneer is probably a couple of hundred dollars a thousand today.

To accommodate small logs, the process and the same fundamental equipment design was used, but the drive mechanisms were redesigned, also the spindle sizes, but the knife configuration and pressure bar configuration changed because of new ideas, not because of necessities. Today, to peel at very high rates of speed, a lot of special equipment is required to handle small cores. Lathe chargers that we know today were not in existence until the 1960s. In the 50s, if you had a forty inch diameter log and you put it in the lathe, it would peel for fifteen to twenty minutes. Today, Coe has a lathe at Willamina, Oregon peeling twenty-two small logs a minute, which is less than three seconds per log. You're trying to get the maximum length of veneer out of a log, so you have to have it centered properly and if you don't you're throwing money away.

One of the new innovations of the early 1950s was the veneer dryer feeder. Ed Parker, the Coe engineer who encouraged me to work for Coe, was the designer. They had built one of these feeders and tested it at a plant in Painesville, and then it was shipped to the West Coast and delivered to Multnomah Plywood on the Willamette River in Portland. It had sat there two years because the company was broke and didn't have the money to finish building the plant. At some point I had talked to a company called Paragon Plywood in Crescent City, California and convinced them to put this dryer feeder in their plant. We shipped it to Crescent City and I put the machine in myself. It was a new plant and had two new dryers, two lathes, all of which I installed and I had been there for some time and I had gotten to know the manager, superintendent, master mechanic and all the people who were involved. They believed in me and I said we can put this dry feeder in and we can save you some labor and money. That particular machine went in and operated throughout the entire life of that plant, which was disassembled in the late 1980s I believe. The plywood plants realized they needed these dryer feeders and they were not cumbersome machines to build. By 1959, one-hundred-fifty Coe feeders were in daily operation. Coe obtained a patent which, in Coe's opinion, was infringed upon, but there were never any significant ramifications.

Many of these dryer feeders were installed on a lease agreement, which was unusual for American industry. The customer usually agreed to rent the machines for four years with rental payments to be made monthly. After that, the monthly rental decreased to a minimal amount. All maintenance and taxes were paid by the lessor (the plywood producer). Coe also leased clippers on the same basis. One key to the situation was that the feeders and the clippers were well integrated machines that could be moved with comparative ease if the lessor failed to pay the rent.

In addition to Coe machinery, we represented and sold Ederer Engineering (cranes), Durand Machine Works (feeding and handling machinery), Laucks Laboratories (instruments), Baldwin-Lima Hamilton (plywood presses) and Williams-White & Company (plywood presses). It became my responsibility to know the fine details of each of their machines and models.

CHAPTER ELEVEN

KENNETH FORD

When I "officially" moved to Oregon in late 1952, I drove across the country to Oregon and my first stop was Dillard, Oregon, home of Roseburg Lumber's new plywood plant project. They were preparing to install two Coe lathes and a dryer and quite a lot of other equipment. Mr. Conway had sold Roseburg this equipment. Coe had a good reputation in those days after the war, and as we grew, we had probably the best machinery in the business and as a result we enjoyed a large percentage of the business.

I arrived at the Roseburg site about 6:30 one night; someone pointed the direction of the new plant building and I drove to it. I got out and began walking through the building from one end to the other, looking around and sizing up the project I would have to start the next day. The roof was on the building, but there was no concrete floors, a few foundations were poured. I had walked to one end and now was making my way back when I saw a figure in the distance. As I came closer to him he asked, who are you and what are you doing here? I told him I was Fred Fields with Coe and that I was supposed to go to work there tomorrow, helping with the installation of the machinery. He identified himself as Kenneth Ford, the owner of the plant and of Roseburg Lumber. I knew that much about Kenneth and I knew he had been a logger and was a hard worker, and I was impressed that he was still out there late at night.

This was going to be Ford and Roseburg's first plywood mill. Kenneth, who had grown up working with his father's logging and lumber business near Lebanon, Oregon, moved to Roseburg and formed Roseburg Lumber in 1936. He built a circle saw sawmill and planer mill out of secondhand machinery and in addition to lumber he sold the sawdust for fuel which was an important part of his income. It wasn't a one man operation, but probably pretty close to it, with Ford as the mill superintendent, head logger and the only salesman. My wife Suzanne's father was in the insurance business back then and he recalled to me some lean years when Kenneth was really having a tough time making ends meet. Also, Kenneth was always an opportunist and probably biting off more than he could chew. Suzanne's father would go down to Roseburg to collect the insurance premiums from Kenneth and said he practically had to chase Kenneth around in the woods and had to wait for him to come down out of a tree to tell him his premium had to be paid. The only problem was Kenneth didn't have any money. Later on I would encounter some similar character traits from Kenneth, except then he had the money.

Kenneth managed to keep the business moving forward, added dry kilns and increased lumber production bit by bit. At the same time he began purchasing area timberland at a cheap cost, which marked the beginnings of what became a substantial timberland holdings that Roseburg continues to maintain today. As the operation at Roseburg grew, Kenneth purchased property at Dillard, Oregon and began building a more modern higher production band mill and drying operation there toward the end of the war. Toward the end of the 1940s the Roseburg mill sustained a major fire that destroyed nearly all of the dry end equipment as well a million board feet of finished lumber inventory. Partial operations at Roseburg were restored as the Dillard mill neared completion and then shut down when the Dillard sawmill went into full production.

It was about this time when I encountered Kenneth for the first time in the shell of his new plywood plant. After our introductions, I told him I had just driven into town and hadn't had anything to eat, and that it was my birthday and would he like to have dinner. He said he hadn't eaten either, but he had a bottle down at the Elk's Club and invited me to join him there for a drink and a bite to eat. We became fast friends quickly and remained so until he passed away.

He completed the Dillard plywood plant, which was called Number One, then a couple of years later built Number Two at Dillard, a very big plant and we sold him a lot of machinery for it. He then purchased the plant in Coquille, Oregon from Textron Smith Wood Products and built a plant in Dixonville outside of Roseburg. In 1965 he completed a particleboard plant in Dillard, the largest plant of its kind in U.S. if not the world. And some years later in 1972 he completed a new plywood plant at Riddle, Ore., which became known as the Super Plant, with the main building a third of a mile long, covering sixteen acres, almost 700,000 square feet under one roof, with a production capacity of 225 million square feet of plywood (3/8 inch basis). His empire, which I guess is what you have to call it, in addition to plywood, expanded with more sawmills, a chip export facility in North Bend, plywood and particleboard finishing plants, another expansion at the particleboard mill and all the while the company's timberland base accelerated tremendously, especially in 1979 with the purchase of 320,000 acres and two sawmills from Kimberly-Clark in northern California and the purchase of 235,000 acres, a sawmill and plywood mill from Diamond Lands in Red Bluff, California in 1988. Employment reached at least 4,000 at one point. Needless to say the logger who couldn't pay his insurance premium eventually came of age.

Not that Kenneth would ever like paying his bills. He always wanted to have one hand in his pocket on his wallet, and the last payments on machinery he wanted to hang onto that for dear life, make sure he got his pound of flesh. Usually he would hold off paying until he wanted something new, a new order, and then as part of the new order you would get the last payment on the last order. He was very resourceful. He and I dealt on a handshake. I don't think he dealt that way with very many people. He was always busy or going somewhere and didn't have too much time. But like I said, we became friends.

As far as dealing with him on projects, he wanted to know every nut and bolt and every bearing, the type of bearing and every minute detail of all the machinery. Even though when you started talking about it he might not know anything about it, by the time he got the order placed he knew all about it, and by the time he got it installed and running, that's when you really had problems because he was the best second guesser in the world. He'd find all sorts of reasons why the darn thing didn't work as he envisioned it.

We liked to spar, but we got along well in that regard for the most part, though we had our moments. I remember we had dinner down at the Multnomah Athletic Club in Portland. We'd had a few drinks and we were walking back to the car, and I can't remember specifically what he said to me but he wasn't going to pay for this and wasn't going to do that. I said Kenneth, we just can't leave this the way it is, you've got to understand you've got to pay for it. We've been friends for a long time and I don't want to walk away from this not continuing to be friends. He could see I was breaking up and he said okay, let's go, we'll get this settled and he sent a check in or whatever it was and the argument was over. We didn't have any fistfights. I wouldn't swing at him if he swung at me. We had plenty of reason to argue, and we did, and it was always about some very specific details. It wasn't an ambiguous question, it was a very specific point. But he was rarely satisfied. If you sold him something and it was new and he didn't know anything about it—and this held true with a lot of people—and he took your word for the abililty to perform a task, well the process of going through the design and building of equipment would take six to eight months. As time expired, he would gain a greater knowledge of what you were trying to accomplish and as his sphere of knowledge increased, he could always find things you were not doing or couldn't do that was not part of the agreement in the first place. He kept trying to move the goal posts. Why can't you do that? Well, that wasn't part of the idea, that's part of the evolution of doing it. Kenneth was an expert in finding ways and means of not being satisfied with what he thought the project was supposed to do. It might be just as simple as using a P235 bearing as opposed to a roller taper bearing, a more sophisticated and expensive bearing. If there was something better for the application he wanted it. If he didn't specify it in the first place we didn't necessarily supply it. He was always looking for a little bit of edge, but he was a perfectionist.

He was about the same in his mannerisms all the time. Some of the media painted a picture of him as a hard-drinking timber baron, but he didn't drink very much. If he went to dinner he might have two drinks. For many many years until he died, we always found some way of getting together for dinner the night after Thanksgiving, usually down in Palm Springs, his wife and my wife included. During those times he might let his hair down a little bit and he was funny in that regard. But I never saw him drunk. He wasn't a hell raiser, and he was too busy to do a lot of entertaining and wasn't inclined to waste time doing that. He wasn't looking for a lot of publicity. He wasn't anxious to talk to the newspapers. He wasn't out there pounding his chest. At times he expressed some bitterness toward media reports that attempted to gauge his net worth. Certainly when he got those plywood mills going his fortunes escalated, so much so that in 1957 Kenneth and his first wife, Hallie, created The Ford Family Foundation, which to this day gives millions of dollars in various scholarship programs. Kenneth also donated tremendous funding to local endeavors such as hospital construction and technologies. I believe Ken-

neth and Hallie divorced in the early 1970s. One of their two children was Allyn, who took over the leadership of the company.
Hallie Ford continued her charitable pursuits as well, and died
only a couple of years ago at age 102. Kenneth later married Bonnie Stanley, who is still living.

As with any company, it wasn't all smooth sailing by any
means. I can remember when he bought a lot of timberland in California from Kimberly-Clark and he paid a terrible price for it.
Prior to that, he had just made an agreement with his outside audi-
tors and his own people that they weren't going to spend any more
money and everything was going to stay as it was because tough
times were coming and the company wouldn't be making any
money and so they weren't going to spend any. The first thing you
know he goes out and buys this tract of timber and borrowed a
fantastic amount of money at the time, and he agreed to pay seventeen percent interest on the loan. I know he shuffled around and
hustled pretty hard to get over that hump. He didn't show his anxiety, but you knew darn well looking at him that he had wished he
hadn't done that. I'll be speaking more on Kenneth Ford as this
book progresses.

While I was selling and installing plywood machinery in the
Northwest during the 1950s, I was also a plywood manufacturer.
I didn't expect to become the next Kenneth Ford, but it was a
very valuable experience. I was actually a part-owner of two
plants, an existing veneer mill we bought in Crescent City, California called Cavneer, from which we shipped veneer to be manufactured into plywood at a new plant we built in Grants Pass,
Oregon. Along with myself, the owners were F. A. Johnson, who
was called Smokey, and Raleigh Chinn, who was a wholesale
distributor of plywood in the Midwest. Smokey ran the business.
I had gotten to know Smokey when he reorganized Multnomah
Plywood in Portland. After he went through that exercise he
decided he wanted to build a plant in Crescent City, but Crescent
City didn't have a railroad, so they decided to build the plywood
plant in Grants Pass, which was on rail siding and they trucked
green veneer from Crescent City to Grants Pass, a distance of

maybe ninety miles. I say "they" when I should be saying "we," though I wasn't hands-on with the business like Smokey was. When he came to me with the idea he said we're going to build this plant, do you want to be a part of it? I told him I would put some money in it and asked him how much he needed. He said I don't know, we'll find out. I was able to negotiate with Coe to buy a dryer and associated equipment. We bought it on terms and paid it off in a normal manner, in two years, at a normal interest rate, which Coe had done many times. The people at Coe knew Smokey to be a good honorable guy and a guy who could make a plant operate.

The veneer plant was an old plant, but we took out the old lathe and put in a new ten foot lathe that really made it a nice plant. For me it just wasn't an investment. I was able to get into the nitty gritty, the bookwork and understand what the costs were of patching a sheet of veneer and what it costs to lay it up and what glue costs were per thousand square feet. So I studied a lot of detail that gave me insight into what made a manufacturing plant go and that helped me when thinking in terms of designing and building new types of equipment for the plants. Smokey, Raleigh and I sold the plant after we operated it seven or eight years. We sold it to Sam Agnew, who was a man who lived in Centralia, Washington and had about a billion board feet of timber in the Brookings, Oregon area. He operated the plants for many years, before passing away, at which time his son, Jay, took over, and he eventually sold the company to Don Deardorff, who operated it as FourPly. Don became very successful and president of American Plywood Association.

CHAPTER TWELVE

DEVELOPMENTS AT COE

Meanwhile Coe Company was experiencing remarkable growth in the 1950s. The company turned 100 years old in 1952. In 1954, Edward Hudak joined Coe as a machine designer. After serving in this capacity for a number of years, he would be appointed chief engineer in 1967 and would supervise the expanded Painesville engineering activities until his retirement in 1986. The busiest year of the decade was 1956 when the company up to that point in its history saw an all-time high in dollar value of shipments.

Frank W. Milbourn, Sr., president of the company since 1920, passed away on April 21, 1957. He had been going to the office every day as far as I knew. The first real change of officers in a long time occurred immediately thereafter. Frank W. Milbourn, Jr. worked closely with his dad and they had a very nice management team, good smart people. Frank Jr. became president. Pat Morris was the executive vice president and sales manager and

Art Holden was the executive vice president in charge of sales in the gypsum board business. Joe Dodds was the secretary treasurer. He had started with Milbourn in 1920. Those people ran the company and when Mr. Milbourn passed away those people stepped in his shoes and there was no question about how the company was going to run.

I wasn't around Mr. Milbourn, Sr. a great deal, but he was a tougher type individual than his son. He was a taskmaster. He was a very bright fellow. He went to the University of Kentucky and was a mechanical engineer and had worked for Southern Engine and Boilers Works before buying Coe Company out of near bankruptcy in 1919. He told me that when he bought the company he had some money and it was in stocks and bonds and he wrapped those stocks and bonds in a *Wall Street Journal*, walked into the bank, laid them down on the loan officer's desk and said here's my collateral and with that he bought the company. He was very good at telling an interesting story. He had good people working with him and around him, though there were some I didn't think all that much of as they continued with the company after his passing away. He was a hard taskmaster and his son grew up under him and had a better and smoother way about him than his father, but his father was a very bright, engineering type and he was aggressive with innovations of his own and his people. And he was successful. He ran the business from 1919 until he passed away in 1957. His son took over from that point and at that point I wasn't sure that his son had enough self-confidence that he wanted to run the business. But he took over, ran the business for a year and he decided, yes, he was going to continue to run the business and he did it well.

Of course Coe Company had a lot going on outside my area. In 1950, a Philippine plywood group had visited the United States, with its expenses being paid largely by the State Department. Fortunately, its itinerary was primarily developed by Coe's export sales office, the United States Machinery Company. These efforts culminated in complete plants including lathes, dryers and other machinery for Santa Clara Lumber Company,

Taggat Sawmills Company, Misamis Lumber Company, Insular Lumber Company, International Hardwoods, Bislig Bay Lumber Company, Aguinaldo Development Company, Mahogany Products and Sta.Inez Plywood Company. The predominant machine in the Philippine plywood expansion was the Coe Model 249 lathe. Only a few of these machines had been sold domestically, but it developed that they were ideally suited for the size and type of logs used in the Philippines.

The export business was good in the other areas too, notably Mexico. Some of the firms to whom machinery was supplied were Plywood Ponderosa de Mexico, S. A., Triplay de Palenque, S. A., Productos Forestales Mexicanos, Duraplay de Parral, S.A.

Tremendous expansion also took place in the plasterboard and fiberboard industries in the 1950s and Coe was the dominant supplier of the equipment to these companies. National Gypsum Company completed its post-war expansion by adding five new plants. Five dryers or major parts thereof were supplied to United States Gypsum Company. Bestwall Gypsum (now Georgia-Pacific) added three large plants. Celotex, Flintkote and Kaiser installed new units.

The gypsum wallboard industry had experienced dynamic growth since its inception in the early 20s. From the very beginning, Coe was involved in finding improved ways to accomplish the drying process. By the late 20s, production had exceeded one billion sq. ft. annually as the result of rather intense marketing efforts. By 1940, this figure had doubled to 2 billion sq. ft. and by 1960 again more than tripled to nearly 8 billion sq. ft. annually. Coe continued to maintain a leadership role in the supply of production line equipment and turnkey projects. Large new fiberboard plants were installed by Celotex, Johns-Manville, Abitibi, Prairie Fiberboard, Barrett and Masonite. The first "Fesco" board (Perlite) was introduced by The Schundler Company of Joliet, Illinois using Coe equipment following a process development at the Coe Springfield, Ohio laboratory. Another first was the tube dryers to dry fiber conduit for the Orangeburg Manufacturing Company, which expanded to the West Coast. All of the above installations included intricate feeding and unloading equipment which were designed and built by Coe. The expansion of the Coe engineering staff in the 1950s was necessary to handle these new and revised products.

While I was out West, in 1957, Coe in Painesville erected a 37,500 square foot new building to house the Assembly Department. This was located on the north side of the main line of the N&S (Norfolk & Southern) Railroad, on the site of the Coe family homestead. The Sheet Metal Department moved from its cramped and decrepit quarters to the building vacated by the Assembly Department. As designs were going more to welded, fabricated structures, a large part of the new assembly building was occupied by the structural department. So in 1958 a new addition comprising 15,000 square feet was added to the building in order to house the structural shop.

My partner Art Conway and I had maintained a profitable business through the 1950s. A big part of it was parts. We bought parts from Coe and resold them. Of course in the parts business we had to inventory those parts and sometimes they would be on the shelves for years and we had to carry those expenses. We received maybe five or six percent commission on the sale of new machinery.

Art Conway died in 1958 after a long association with Coe dating back to 1927. His son, Jim, who was still in our business, had started a wholesale sporting goods business. I think Jim had read between the lines that if his dad wasn't there that his future relationship would Coe might subside. So he said to me, "Why don't we sell to Coe? Coe wants to build a West Coast plant." We all agreed to that and that's when in July of 1959 Coe bought out Jim Conway and myself, Conway & Fields. I was appointed Coe's Western manager.

The "plant" that Jim Conway had referred to that Coe wanted to build stemmed from discussions I had been having with Frank Milbourn, Jr. for several years. I thought Coe should have a little plant on the West Coast to show our intent and purpose in serving the business in the Northwest and people would rely on our technology and ideas developed in the Northwest. With a small plant we could provide parts and service and we could also design new small machines that might come to my mind or might even design machines that the customer had envisioned. It was a matter of getting ourselves a little closer to the woods so to speak and accommodating ideas that came from the field, from the manufacturers of the product. There were all sorts of old Swedes out there in the Northwest that had ideas coming out of their ears, but they didn't have too many people to listen to them. I came along and a lot of them shared their thoughts with me and we got a little bit of a reputation and before long we had people like Weyerhaeuser and Georgia-Pacific coming to us with some of their ideas on how they could improve their manufacturing processes. We had working agreements with G-P and Weyerhaeuser for a long long time.

After Mr. Milbourn, Sr. passed away and then Mr. Conway died, and after Frank Jr. had been in charge for a while, he decided that he had a good firm grasp on the company and was anxious to get the company moving. He decided maybe what we ought to do is expand like that guy Fields out on the West Coast has suggested. The first thing we did was to look around and see if we couldn't find a similar business to buy. I talked with companies like Globe, Ederer and four or five other companies and there wasn't anybody really ready to sell. I went about seeing if I could find a company who had the facilities, maybe not in our business, any business, who had machinery and an office and some space to expand in. The only thing that was available was old antiquated plants; we wanted something that was going to make Coe look like Coe. We decided to give that up but find a piece of property, which we did, ten acres in Tigard, Oregon, several miles south of Portland. The intent was for the Tigard plant to enable us to manufacture a few simple things but also to have and continue to expand our repair parts and service business.

When we got the plant up, I remember very well that we had a small engine lathe that we had shipped from Painesville that they weren't using much. We also had a welding machine or two and we had an ironworker which we used to fabricate the steel components for parts of various description. In the meantime back in the late 40s we had a warehouse on Southeast Sixth Avenue in Portland where we stocked a sizeable amount of repair parts for machinery so they didn't have to wait on parts from Painesville. That parts business was moved out of the warehouse into this new plant and that was the basis of our business in the early stages. We moved into the new facility in 1960. We didn't have a large staff in the West. In addition to myself, we had a couple of guys in the parts department, one in the service department and a secretary. Soon we expanded our staff that included Norton Oehling, Chuck Oliver, Ralph Gage and Ben Bole, all experienced Coe people. Soon after I was made a vice president for Coe and that was a good challenge for me and opened up some opportunities.

It wasn't long after we built the plant at Tigard that I had lunch with Jack Beaman, who was the president of the Douglas Fir Plywood Association and was the sales manager for Southern Oregon Plywood. His office wasn't too far from ours and I would call him and go have lunch. It was sort of a monumental day for we in the machinery business. Prior to that time the only people invited to the plywood association meetings were members of the association and some glue manufacturers such as Borden Chemical and American Marietta. I said to Jack, you're always looking for more members and a way to increase your revenue, why don't you consider allowing Coe to become an associate member of the DFPA. We'll pay some dues. We'd like to attend your meetings and understand some of industry's problems and maybe that will help us design machinery that accommodates or solves some of the problems industry might have. He said by golly I think that's a pretty good idea. He said I'll take that to the board. About two months later he called me and said you're now an associate member of the plywood association. The dues for the existing member mills was based on the amount of production the plant had. So they established a flat rate for us to pay. I don't really know why, but Coe was the only machinery company in the group for four or five years or so. That was just fine with me because none of our competitors were invited. It was a good move on our part.

The Douglas Fir Plywood Association had been formed in 1933. There were few plants around at that time—Aircraft Plywood plant in Seattle that was purchased by U.S. Plywood; Aberdeen Plywood, West Coast Plywood, and the Tucker estates built a huge plant right at the beginning of the war in Lebanon, Oregon, called Cascade Plywood. Even by the end of the war there were probably less than twenty plants. All of them prospered during the war other than having a tough time getting labor. But they had timber cheap and could produce a lot of material. The Douglas Fir Plywood Association did a good job early on with promoting plywood as a standardized commodity and establishing an industry-wide trademark.

So there was a lot going on in my life in the late 1950s and early 1960s. Selling Conway and Fields to Coe. Building a new plant in Tigard. And meeting Suzanne Schoenfeldt. I had met Suzanne in Portland. She was a native of Portland and we were married in the fall of 1958, now more than fifty years ago. We bought a house in Portland, traded her car off, bought her a new car and traveled from Portland on our honeymoon to Phoenix, spent a week there and then caught a plane to Painesville. I introduced Suzanne to the Coe family and we spent a week in Painesville. Her only sibling was her brother, the Rev. Arthur Schoenfeldt, who became very renown for his spiritual work. He studied theology at Holy Cross College in Washington, DC and was ordained a priest in St. Mary's Cathedral in Portland. He served as a chaplain at a high school in Mountain View, Calif. for many years and for the last thirty years of his life he served the University of Portland and was beloved by generations of students. He was known as "Padre." He died in late 2007 in Holy Cross House, Notre Dame-South Bend and the funeral mass was held in the basilica of the Sacred Heart at Notre Dame. During the last twenty years of his life he worked on a book depicting the life of David Dunne, who was his and my wife's grandfather on their mother's side, and at the same time told the history of Portland during the immediate decades before the beginning of the twentieth century and the early decades into the new century. He had nearly finished the book when he died, and left instructions for his peers to complete and publish it, which they did. In 2008 Suzanne and I provided a financial gift to the University of Portland to put toward the construction of two residence halls, one of which is called Rev. Arthur Schoenfeldt, C.S.C. Hall.

I lost my mother in 1961 at age 69. She was still renting out the farmland, but she lived on the farm until she passed away. The farmhouse was home to her. She had stayed healthy and vibrant and she always had a flower garden and even in her later years she raised vegetables if she could get somebody to turn up the soil and get the beds prepared. Somebody was always around to help her do those things. The only time I ever saw her in the hospital was on her death bed. She died in Elwood, Indiana and is buried beside my father and other family members. She left the farm to my sister, Marienne, who continued to rent out the land.

CHAPTER THIRTEEN

PLYWOOD GONE SOUTH

The 1960s was a decade of numerous product and machinery innovations in the wood products industry. One oft-forgotten was the transition from cold press to hot press. Before World War II the only people who used a hot press were the ones using exterior glue in order to make plywood that could be exposed to the elements such as in a boat or plane. One such company was Aircraft Plywood in Seattle. There were one or two other plants that had hot presses and it required a hot press to set the glue for an exterior glue line.

Most of the plywood that was produced in those days was produced in a cold press and a cold press had no heat applied to the panel as the glue was setting up. No heating in between the platens. As time went on plywood became widely used in places where it should not have been used. They would take plywood that was produced in a cold press and take it out on a job where the houses were being built and set it outside and if it happened to rain it would cause all the plywood to start delaminating and plywood became a negative name in the industry. People in the lumber business gloated on that. Plywood's place was limited to only sub floors and other interior applications.

In the early 60s, generally through the Douglas Fir Plywood Association, the industry agreed to produce all exterior plywood with exterior glue, which meant that every plant had to buy a new hot press. The hot press became a very hot subject in those days, no pun intended, and there were probably seven or eight different manufacturers of hot presses. As a result of this new emphasis, all plywood could be used inside or outside, for farm buildings or for siding like tongue and groove and t1-11 siding and then there was plywood that had rough finishes. There had been hot presses manufactured for years so it wasn't new technology; the newest technology came in the performance of the glue. In the early days if you were going to press quarter-inch plywood, you would press two panels to an opening in a press and the pressing time would be in the six to seven minute time frame. As time went on and as glue manufacturers developed better types of adhesives, the pressing times got down to three minutes. As the press time decreased, then that would allow them to use more openings in the press. Originally they started with 12 to 16 openings then it got to 20 and 24 and 30 and 36 and up to 40. And there were one or two presses in the U.S. with 46 or 48 openings, but it was hard to keep a 40-opening press full. As gluing the panels took so much time for the labor or automatic layup machines to accumulate forty panels, you limited the size of the press to the arrangement you had for gluing the panels together.

Somebody asked me not long ago if I had any involvement in the southern pine plywood movement. I'll state here what I said then: I was involved right up to my ears.

The first company that looked into manufacturing southern pine plywood and began building a plant was Kirby Forest Industries at Silsbee, Texas. Then Georgia-Pacific started building a plant at Fordyce, Arkansas and may have made the first plywood produced before Kirby, but both of them were producing southern pine plywood in 1964. Kirby came out west and they had selected an engineer who had done a lot of design-and-build plants on the West Coast, Del Collinson. He directed Kirby to us. They wanted to ship a good size supply of logs to the West Coast to make them into plywood to see if it was feasible. I arranged to have that test conducted at the U.S. Plywood plant in Roseburg. That was done through the assistance of Marshall Leeper, who was a good friend of mine. We had several railcar loads of logs shipped out. Steaming of logs was just becoming a way of life and the plant in Roseburg had good steaming facilities and that's the reason we did the tests at that plant. We took those logs at Roseburg and ran them through the peeling, drying, pressing, sawing and sanding operations there. Mind you, this was all done in cooperation with Douglas Fir Plywood Association and they took samples of the plywood to Tacoma and ran their testing procedures and made a report to Kirby that indicated this was a very practical thing to do. Now this was a year or two before Kirby's plant was ever completed. There was an awful lot of work, a lot of shuffling around, trying to determine what change in machinery should be made, what gluing problems that were presented, and a whole myriad of questions that would be asked in a new process.

Almost simultaneously, Jens Jorgensen, vice president of plywood production at Georgia-Pacific, had picked up a few carloads of logs and sent them to their plant in Coquille, Oregon and run a few tests of his own to see if they could peel it and if it would stick together. Jens was a good friend of mine. In the meantime Kirby was going through this process of evaluation, whether they should build the plant or not. They had just spent $19 million building a new sawmill in Silsbee, Texas and that was sort of choking in their throat because they hadn't made a lot of money out of it. Kirby was owned by Santa Fe Railroad and they had to dot every "i" and cross every "t" so it took them a long time to get organized. In the meantime they ordered the machinery from us, which was 95% of the machinery for the plant, including an eight foot lathe and two dryers. Then Jens came along and he said G-P wanted to order some machinery for their plant, including an eight foot lathe, a four foot lathe and two dryers. He didn't tell us where he was going to build it; he said we'll tell you where we're going to build it when the machinery is made. Anyway, we shipped to both companies probably within a few months of each other. But G-P had their own engineer, Bill Peters, doing their own engineering and they went right ahead and got the plant built in Fordyce. I remember the first day they started up, I wasn't there, but Jens called me. We had a lathe charger, which in those days was a very new device, and he said it wasn't working very well and wasn't setting logs precisely on center and I'll always remember saying he didn't need the phone because I could hear him from Fordyce yelling at me. He said "Damn it, if you don't get that thing fixed in 24 hours you better be on your damn way down here!" I got on the next airplane and fortunately it was fixed before I got there.

There were all sorts of problems in southern pine plywood. Many of them related to the wood itself. It had a tendency to warp a great deal. The press G-P put in was a Columbia press; it only had three inches of daylight and they had a heck of a time poking a loose panel into the daylight openings. Fortunately that wasn't our problem but it did impair the overall startup of the plant. In the meantime Kirby was plodding along in their normal fashion and they got their plant up and running and it started up pretty well. We had the experience of Fordyce and our service people and technicians were able to take advantage of what they had learned over there and Kirby got started up pretty darn nicely. They were probably a little more organized than G-P but they didn't have the experienced people like G-P. Georgia-Pacific just picked up a whole shift of people from a Western plant and sent them to Fordyce and they had experienced people throughout the plant; even the glue mixer was an experienced guy. But Kirby had to hire guys out of the sawmill. They had Bud Stevens who was the superintendent and had come out of the IP plant in Florence, Oregon. Tom Orth was the chief executive of Kirby at the time.

One of the key things that happened during this period was the role of the Douglas Fir Plywood Association in bringing together Western and Southern industry members and coming up with a single national manufacturing standard. This really aided the industry's promotional efforts. At the same time, Douglas Fir Plywood Association changed its name to American Plywood Association in 1964 to reflect the fact that the plywood industry was now national in scope.

There was some adjustment going from manufacturing Douglas fir plywood to southern pine plywood. The roller bar we had been using right at the point of cutting the veneer didn't work too well on southern pine so we had to use a solid nosebar, similar to a hardwood lathe peeling birch or gum. It was a matter of the adjustment of the equipment to accommodate the wood. We were trying to take a very rough wood, southern pine, which grows about twice as fast as fir; the growth rings are twice as far apart, which means when you peel it the softwood between the hard spots often breaks loose and it causes the veneer to become too rough for an acceptable use. It meant changing the method of heating the log; eventually they got to the point of boiling logs, putting them in submerged water and cooking it as opposed to blowing hot steam on the outside of a log. Those were mill problems and not specifically related to the machinery involved. Southern pine had a lot of water, twice the amount of water in a log as a piece of Douglas fir, and about the same amount of water as a piece of ponderosa pine or Idaho white pine, so it took twice as long to dry the veneer in those days. Thus the drying techniques were changed through experience.

A lot of people were apprehensive about this new industry of southern pine plywood, but there were also a lot of the companies who had headquarters in the Northwest who owned or had access to timber down South. They didn't hesitate to go down there and build a plant. Many major companies in the Northwest, Weyerhaeuser, Boise, Georgia-Pacific, U.S. Plywood, Willamette Industries, were the ones who wound up with most of the plants in the South. You can't forget that much of the timber down South was privately owned and mostly available to purchase, as compared to the Northwest where much of the timber was owned by the federal or state government and was coming under greater public scrutiny.

Georgia-Pacific produced its first southern pine plywood in February 1964 and the boom was on, with G-P leading the way. G-P was so instrumental in this movement that I feel compelled to provide a little background on the company up until that point in time.

Owen Cheatham started the company in 1927 in Augusta, Georgia as a hardwood lumber wholesale business. It was called Georgia Hardwood Lumber Company. A few years later he hired a financial whiz kid out of Virginia Polytechnic Institute named Bob Pamplin. VPI was also Cheatham's alma mater, and Pamplin had roomed with Cheatham's brother there.

Cheatham and Pamplin added a line of Southern sawmills to the wholesaling business, but real expansion didn't occur until after World War II. Their first big move was raising $800,000 at a public offering. Then they bought a plywood plant in Bellingham, Washington with the money in 1947. They added two more plywood mills in the Northwest a year later and changed the company's name to Georgia-Pacific Plywood & Lumber Company.

The company boomed in the 1950s and began building a massive timberland base in the Northwest, borrowing a lot of money to do it. They bought C.D. Johnson Lumber in Toledo, Oregon. They moved headquarters from Georgia to Olympia, Washington and then to Portland, Oregon in 1954. A couple of years later, now named Georgia-Pacific Corp., they acquired Coos Bay Lumber in Oregon and Hammond Lumber in northern California and acquired vast amounts of old-growth Douglas fir and redwood as part of those deals. Then a year later G-P entered the pulp and paper business by building a mill at Toledo, Oregon and added numerous paper facilities over the next several years. Pamplin was president by now and people like Robert Flowerree and Bill Hunt had joined the company in the 1950s.

Then the company made two acquisitions that set up its entry into southern pine plywood. G-P bought Crossett Lumber and 560,000 acres in Arkansas and in 1963 bought Fordyce Lumber and 160,000 acres again in Arkansas.

After G-P got their Fordyce plant going, it was less than a year later that Jens Jorgensen called me one day. His office was in Coquille but he also kept an office in Portland at G-P. He called me and said I'd like to see you at one o'clock. He was a very gruff guy, and he didn't wait for any excuses, such as no I can't make it. He said, I'll see you at one o'clock tomorrow at my office in Portland. The next day I was sitting in the lobby about a quarter till one and I'm thinking Jens is going to chew me out for some damn thing. All of the sudden the elevator door opened and Bill Hunt, who was president, and Jens walked out. Bill was always a very friendly guy to me. He said, "Hi Freddie, how are you? Listen, Jens has something important to talk to you about. I'll let you guys go on with your business, let's see if we can't get this thing on the move."

I went back to Jens' office, and he said, you know, I don't want to talk about it now but I want you to get me a proposal together for two lathes and three dryers for each of five plants. We're going to get this going right away. The lathes consist of one eight foot, one four foot, the dryers to be a certain size, you get all that together, and I'd like to see it in two days and we'll get going. I did just that.

I was about dumbfounded. He didn't say where the plants were going. He sat there and wrote out an order on a couple pages of purchase order paper for five plants.

Less than a year's time passed and Jens called again. He said, I want to see you. I went to meet him. He said I want to order five more plants. We went through the same routine, made a few changes in machine specs and so forth and we got that going. A few months later he called and said I want to order five more plants.

Fifteen plywood plants! That was the biggest order Coe ever had. That's the biggest order industry had ever heard of. G-P had the team in place to pull it off. Bob Pamplin was the chairman and he was the one who found a place to park a plant where he had a decent chance of outbidding everybody else for timber. Bill Hunt was there to sell the product and Jens to build the plants. Between myself and Coe and those fellas from G-P, we got the job done. We put in a new office in Atlanta and sent Ralph Gage down there to be hands-on, which worked out well. Ralph had grown up in Painesville, went to Ohio State and played quarterback and defensive back on their national championship team in 1957. The two Milbourn sons were good friends of his so he went to Coe looking for a job and they gave him one. He worked in the shop as an assistant to the superintendent for a couple of years and then came out to Portland and worked for us and got some experience. We asked him to move down to Atlanta and he became very effective, sometimes more vocal than was appropriate, but nevertheless he worked hard at it and did a good job. Jens had sent down Art West, who was the manager of G-P's Springfield plant and he became the head of their southern pine operations out of Crossett, where they had their two biggest plants. G-P built up a staff in the south and we built up a staff in the south and we just did those things that were necessary to be done. And we all did it very fast. It's really rather mind-boggling when you think about it. In 1965, the year after the Fordcye plant started up, G-P was producing plywood at its plant in Crossett, then in 1966 started up a second plant in Crossett as well as plants in Louisville, Mississippi; Emporia, Virginia and Savannah, Georgia. It started up plants in Gloster, Mississippi and Chiefland, Florida in 1967, and at Russellville, South Carolina and Cedar Springs, Georgia in 1968, at Gloster and Taylorsville, Mississippi in 1969 and at Monticello, Georgia and Urania, Louisiana in 1970, and there were many more to come in the 1970s.

The great thing about Georgia-Pacific's three orders of five plants each was that our end of it was fairly streamlined. Number one, as we went along, the engineering for the machinery was basically done. It had to be re-engineered to suit the specific plant's conditions and environment, but basically the lathes were designed and the chargers in those days were pretty simple and the other auxiliary equipment around the lathe was standard—what we would normally use in the West only smaller in size. We were just getting into the jet dryer design in the early 1960s. After that first plant at Fordyce, which had the standard West Coast type dryer, we started installing jet dryers. Also keep in mind that we were not only getting G-P's business, but we were getting business from Kirby, Temple, Columbia Plywood and others. We increased the production and had to do some subcontract work. We added two shifts in those departments where we needed to. We would only run a second shift under unusual conditions in years past, but this became a steady diet of second shift work, which meant we had quite a few new employees. But as I say, we had the engineering done, and that is always a big problem in getting new machinery orders manufactured and delivered in time. It being basic standard machinery for us, we were able to move rather quickly into the manufacturing. A lot of it was done in Painesville, probably eighty percent.

Georgia-Pacific was certainly putting together a southern pine plywood empire so to speak. But there would be consequences for their actions. As part of their plan, Georgia-Pacific was buying up small timber companies in the South along with a lot of timberland, and putting in distribution centers to support its growing lineup of plywood plants. G-P also raised the price of timber in doing it and the small operations started complaining that as a result G-P was putting them out business. In 1971 the Federal Trade Commission stepped in and claimed G-P had tied up all the good locations in the South for plywood plants and thus substantially lessened competition. In other words, the FTC said G-P was creating a monopoly.

G-P fought this charge for some while and then Pamplin, who was chairman and president (Owen Cheatham having retired in 1968), came up with a fairly remarkable plan that would fend off a total decimation of G-P's southern pine plywood business. He proposed a spin-off of certain G-P assets and properties and the formation of a new company, which would compete against G-P and everybody else. The FTC agreed and thus Louisiana-Pacific was created in January 1973.

L-P received assets worth $327 million, about 20% of G-P's value. The majority of the properties were sawmills in the West, about two dozen of them, as well as a half million acres of timberland. Though the FTC's accusation had centered on G-P's monopoly of southern pine plywood, G-P gave up only three southern pine plywood mills, at Urania, Louisiana and at New Waverly and Corrigan, Texas. G-P also gave up a particleboard plant in Urania and one under construction in Corrigan.

The rest of the story is that G-P also spun off the men who would lead Louisiana-Pacific. Harry Merlo was an executive vice president of G-P over Western operations. Merlo had grown up working at a small sawmill in Cloverdale, California and eventually bought into the company, and G-P eventually bought that company and Merlo had come with it. Merlo helped to develop G-P's lumber operations in the West, but he soon felt stagnated at G-P and made it known to Pamplin that he would like to buy some of the G-P properties in the West. Merlo's proposal to Pamplin led to Pamplin's much bigger spin-off scheme involving L-P and Merlo. Merlo became became president and chief operating officer of L-P. He took with him operating people like Jim Eisses and Ronnie Paul. Bill Hunt, who had served as president of G-P and become vice chairman of the G-P board, and who was getting pretty close to retirement, moved from G-P to L-P as chairman and CEO and served in that capacity for a couple of years before retiring, at which point Merlo took over everything. It was neither lumber nor plywood however on which Merlo and L-P left their greatest mark. That would come some years later with a product L-P called waferwood, which later became better known as oriented strandboard. I usually see Harry once a year. Same ole Harry. We get along fine. He still has an ego about the size of all outdoors.

One company that didn't make the move to southern pine plywood was Roseburg Lumber in Oregon. Kenneth Ford took a look at it, but never made the leap. He wrote me the following letter late in 1964, after Georgia-Pacific, Kirby and Temple had begun production at their southern pine plywood plants.

December 4, 1964
Dear Fred:
I just finished talking to Frank Spears and during our conversation he stated that he talked to you a few days ago and that you indicated the profitability of a Southern Plywood Plant looked good.

As you know, I had our accountant work up a pro-forma of a proposed plywood plant in the South. Not that it makes a great deal of difference, the report which they prepared is not what you would call lucrative. I am enclosing a copy of this report and wish you would please go over same and if you find that it is grossly in error, wish you would please get hold of Dave Castles and see if we can get the report corrected as I want to use the report in two or three places soon after the first of the year.

Very truly yours
Kenneth W. Ford,
President

CHAPTER FOURTEEN

ADVANCEMENTS IN TECHNOLOGY

Coe's technologies continued to evolve during the 1960s. One of these was the jet veneer dryer. Another was the dual spindle lathe.

The company entered into some basic research in the field of drying and employed Battelle Institute of Columbus, Ohio as consultants. This led to the building of the Vert-A-Jet dryer, which was a complete revolution in the drying of veneer. In this process, hot air was directed in a perpendicular direction above and below the veneer to be dried, whereas in the past a longitudinal air flow had been used. The movement of this air required more electrical horsepower, but the drying time of any given species of wood was reduced by approximately one-half, thereby decreasing the length of dryer required for any given species by approximately one-half. A commercial-sized gas-fired Vert-A-Jet dryer was installed at the Painesville plant so that full scale drying experiments could be conducted.

As with any technology, we were constantly trying to improve on it as it gained more plant hours. In 1967 we contracted Battelle Institute to conduct a study on possible improvements to the dryer. Coe's Pat Morris wrote me the following letter upon the release of the study. I think it provides a good example of what was going on in those days as Coe and its engineers pushed forward.

October 19, 1967

Dear Fred,

During your telephone conversation of October 18 with Frank Milbourn you advised that Harold Erickson informed you that Weyerhaeuser Company plans to ship some softwood veneers to their plant in Sault Ste. Marie for drying in the Proctor dryer in that plant. You advised that Erickson is of the opinion that in our cable type in-line dryer with jet air system we should be able to reduce drying times which are being used at the present time. We agree that considerable thought should be given to methods of reducing the drying times now being used in our veneer dryers. One very important factor is determining maximum temperature which can be used in various stages of the dryer without damage to the veneer. It must also be recognized that with the softwood veneers there is an extreme variation in the texture, also in the original wet moisture content, and these variables do present a problem for rapid drying of the veneers.

During the past several months we have been working with Battelle Memorial Institute of Columbus, Ohio in connection with this problem of determining most efficient method of obtaining faster drying times. They have made theoretical calculations based on limited amount of actual data and recently presented a report dated July 31, 1967, a copy of which is enclosed.

Recently, Mr. Hazard, of Battelle, visited with us in Painesville, at which time we had the opportunity of discussing their report of July 31. During this discussion there was considerable doubt concerning the calculated information in their report concerning the use of 1/4" diameter jets spaced on 1-1/2" centers as compared to the use of slots. With reference to their report I have noted question marks on Pages 10, 18 and 19.

In general their data and other data which we have obtained indicate that with the jet type dryers an increase in temperature throughout the dryer of 10° will give an increase in capacity of approximately 5 percent, and that it is necessary to double the volume of air in order to obtain an increase of approximately 33 percent. This clearly indicates that the most economical way of reducing the drying time is by the use of the maximum temperature without damage to the veneer.

As you know, we are in the process of designing an experimental dryer with enclosed length consisting of three sections, each 6'-0" long, and each six foot long section equipped with an extra large jet air system. When this machine is built we would be in position to make tests with temperatures up to 600° and with air volume or velocity from our present amount to an amount some three times the present amount. It will, however, be several months before we have this dryer erected and ready for testing.

The enclosed copy of Battelle's report of July 31, 1967 is extremely confidential.

Yours very truly,
E. P. Morris

Pat Morris was a great guy, a real southern gentleman. Very patient. He was a good sales guy. He always backed me up. He was one of those who hired me.

Veneer dryer feeders and unloaders became standard equipment. A veneer dryer feeder eliminated one man per shift, and it also made it possible to keep a dryer full of veneer, thereby increasing capacity. Unloaders eliminated a great amount of veneer breakage. All new dryers were installed with feeders and unloaders and these auxiliaries were added to most existing dryers.

The acceptance of jet drying by the plywood industry sparked another idea. Weyerhaeuser and Coe worked together to develop the "in-line" process. In this process, the veneer was peeled in the usual manner, but after going through a tray system it was fed directly into a continuous dryer. The grain of the veneer remained perpendicular to the direction of travel just as it came from the lathe. It was conveyed on cables, and while being so conveyed, it was dried by jet streams above and below the veneer. Then after drying, the veneer ribbon was clipped. Savings in labor and material were evident in the in-line process. Weyerhaeuser installed six "in-line" plants and four other large producers followed suit, namely, Hines, Arkla, Louisiana Plywood and Great Southern.

Dual spindle lathes were operating in the plywood industry in the 1950s, but the first really practical dual spindle lathes came into service on the West Coast about 1963. Coe had developed a good mechanical log charger to go with these lathes. This lathe-charger combination enabled economical processing of smaller logs into commercial veneer and plywood. The combination of these machines with much more efficient electrical lathe drives produced a phenomenal production unit. A lot of credit for these successful innovations was due to the electrical engineers who developed the power and hydraulic control systems.

While the size of most logs in the Pacific Northwest was continuously decreasing, the average southern pine peeler log was still smaller, usually twelve inches or less. The economical processing of small southern pine logs was made possible by well engineered, high speed, dual spindle lathes, chargers and the auxiliary equipment that went with them.

I should mention several hires I made out West that proved very beneficial to Coe and the development of our products in the 1960s and 1970s. I hired Charlie Bamford to design a mechanical lathe charger for us, which is what we sold to Georgia-Pacific in those early years of southern pine plywood. There had been an old Ederer charger, which was a pair of yokes that rolled in and out; they weren't very good. There was another one made by Nicholson, which was a roller type; they had one in at Medford Plywood. That wasn't all that successful either; they sold maybe a half dozen. It didn't improve the speed of anything and the accuracy wasn't very good. Before that, and you would still see this now and then in later years, you charged the log with a pair of tong dogs, a dog on each end of the log and each end was tended by a man and you picked it up with an overhead crane and carried it into the lathe and you centered it after you got to the lathe spindles. You would raise one end or the other to put it in the right position and you would swing the log to and fro to get it positioned as nearly as a guy could guess. It was still a guess. Some of the better operators could do that with one man, but it wasn't very accurate, but that's the way it was in those days.

Another hire I made later in the late 1960s was Gene Knokey. Gene was a very effective guy, knew the business, had managed two or three plywood plants before coming to Coe. He became Coe's vice president of western operations. In later years his son, Alan Knokey, came to work for us. I also hired Art McGee, in 1973. He became head of engineering. He was a very very smart guy, very innovative, very much involved in the design of the X-Y charger and all the other improvements we put on lathes. And there were a lot of improvements when you consider that in the old days the lathes would turn 100 RPM and this was increased to 500 RPM, peeling small logs, six to seven inch in diameter, twenty-two logs a minute and having a full scan every one-tenth of an inch throughout the length and diameter of the log. Bright fellas like Gene and Art helped Coe to make these constant improvements throughout Coe's product line.

I wouldn't say Coe had the run of the market in those years, but we worked hard and we got what we deserved. We had proven performance, we had equipment to demonstrate, we had good value, we had service and we had the best technology.

What more do you need? We probably doubled our revenue in the 1960s and 1970s and increased our employment by 150 percent to maybe 300 people. We got to almost 800 employees eventually. We increased our manufacturing facilities. We added a new building in Painesville, a sheet metal manufacturing facility, and added a new section in Portland, which increased our manufacturing facilities by twenty percent.

Another thing we did in the late 1960s was acquire two companies with significant history in our industry. In 1967, Coe bought Skoog Manufacturing Company of Olympia, Washington. Skoog had come up with the veneer patching machine. We immediately started making this machine in the Portland plant. Then in 1969 we purchased Tidland sander from Tidland Manufacturing of Camas, Washington. All that work was done in Portland as well. Several Tidland employees joined Coe in Portland. These purchases expanded our product line, which meant that even in slow times we usually had work in one product or another. So by 1970, Coe could manufacture or sell about everything needed to build a plywood plant, and we could render good service from our established locations in Painesville, Portland and Atlanta.

The 1970s saw continued product development, such as the veneer stitcher and the Model 72 dryer. Sales of the patching machine and the sander increased dramatically as did the sales of other products that were sold—although not manufactured—by Coe. Notable among these were Redco electric drives, Williams-White presses, American loading and unloading equipment, and a little later the Hombak flaker for particleboard mills.

Not all the machinery development turned out to be a big success. The veneer stitcher was a good example. That was a development by Weyerhaeuser and we worked with them on it. We built eight or ten of them. Originally they were built to sew dry veneer together. That was fine excepting that dry veneer was very abusive to the needles. If the veneer was thick it would break the needles. One night I had the wild idea of sewing green veneer together. I called Gene Knokey and said I have the best idea, let's sew that veneer together before drying instead of after. Let's go to Longview tonight and talk to the foreman and see if he'll let us run some green veneer. We did that on a Monday night and it worked great. We took the veneer and ran it through the dryer and the only problem was the veneer would shrink about six percent and it would create gaps between the pieces of veneer and that was not acceptable by the APA standard. The idea was to take narrow pieces of veneer and put them together to form 4x8 sheets. The idea and the basic plan was very good, but the success of the stitching wasn't very good. It did the same thing as the veneer composer later on. The difference is that in a composer it's done after the veneer has been dried, and it's done with hot melt and string. The machine is very complicated, and being complicated it's also a big maintenance problem. It's still somewhat questionable as to whether it's a practical solution for the problem.

We had a number of development agreements with Weyerhaeuser through the years. They had two or three engineers who were very good and they had no veneer equipment to work with other than what they bought and put into production, but we had facilities to make the various devices and so we joined their ideas with ours ideas and we set about putting them together. Later on we developed a core drive really through the efforts of Harold Erickson and Byran Bookhauser of Weyerhaeuser Central Engineering Department in Tacoma and Art McGee and Gene Knokey of Coe Company.

The core drive was helpful in maintaining the stable position of the log as it was peeled. It was an important development. The main thrust in that was we started out many years ago peeling logs and when we kicked the core out of the spindles it was usually eight to ten inches in diameter. Today we start with a log that's eight to ten inches in diameter, so we're peeling to a much smaller diameter, but to do that, the core once it gets down below six inches it becomes sort of like a string of spaghetti; it's not very stable, and so we put a core drive in the center of the core to apply very precise position of those rolls to keep it in the perfect relationship to the knife so that it would peel veneer of a constant thickness from the outside diameter of the log to the very minimum diameter and from one end of the log to the other end. So it was a very sophisticated positioning device for three separate rolls that would resist the bending of the core as the log was peeling and these three rolls would apply pressure that would resist the force that was created by the knife in cutting the veneer from the log. There were various types of core drives in the early years. Originally there were only two rolls and they were only 18 inches long. A modern core drive has three rolls and those rolls are more like 48 inches in length. They're not precisely the same length because of mechanical interferences with the mechanism. Anyway they're fairly close in length and as I say they're positioned very precisely through the use of the scanning apparatus that we used and with the scanning comes the computer that utilizes the information from the scanner and it in turn positions the log, what some people call the temposonic cylinders which are positioning hydraulic cylinders which apply pressure and can be positioned to within a few thousandths of an inch in relationship to the expected dimensions.

We put that in Longview with the understanding that if it worked we would build the next ten for them. We put it in and it worked, but they wouldn't buy the next ten and they wouldn't let us sell to anyone else so we just sat and stewed and finally they said if you think they work that well you go ahead. The only problem they had was they had a plant manager in Longview who couldn't see the difference with or without a core drive and Weyerhaeuser backed away from them. We sold a lot of them and then Weyerhaeuser came along and said we're supposed to have the right to buy those things. I said okay, all you have to do is send us an order.

There was the 765 charger design that was originally envisioned by Harold Erickson, the engineer for Weyerhaeuser and he had two or three other engineers who worked with him. We built a prototype model of it and convinced ourselves it would be successful for small diameter logs. We designed that and we paid royalties to Weyerhaeuser, some appreciable amount of money. But it was not computerized and it did not have scanners on it, strictly a mechanical apparatus that clamped on the log and got it pretty close to center. We sold twenty-five or thirty of those.

Weyerhaeuser also had an idea of drying veneer with a platen, like a hot press. We weren't involved in the development but we became involved after they built a full scale machine that went into Longview. They must have spent three or four million dollars on it, but we couldn't see the advantage of it and we backed out of it. They were sort of half mad at us.

We talked with them about an agreement on a big roller bar development that we eventually made. They had one that was a smaller roller bar installed in Longview, but we found if you got a bigger roller bar it was much better. We didn't go through the agreement with them and we developed a bigger one and got patents on that and that sort of upset them.

We also had worked with Weyerhaeuser on their layup system. They had a layup system at Snoquamish Falls. It was a lot of clap trap, a lot of devices wiggling here and there. They had that one and built two for the North Bend plant. That was not very satisfactory, but we had an agreement from there on that if we could sell them to somebody else we had that right to do that. We had never sold any and never had any real prospects except we were hoping Weyerhaeuser would buy a few more. In the meantime Georgia-Pacific had built in their own shop several of them for their own use.

Gene Knokey and I were up in Vancouver BC and we were on our way back to Portland. We got down to about Bellingham, Washington and we called the office and the girl said Jens Jorgensen called you. I called him right away. He always talked very loud. He said Fred, you know we've been thinking about maybe turning a license over to somebody to build our layup systems. I said Jesus Jens, I wish I had talked to you a year ago. We have an agreement with Weyerhaeuser. He said hell their system isn't any good, I've seen it, but if you're committed, that's okay. I said I'm afraid we are, we sure appreciate you thinking of us. That was the end of that, excepting when Georgia-Pacific moved their headquarters from Portland to Atlanta, and they had their machinery division located next to us in Portland for sale. We bought it and the right to build their layup system. Weyerhaeuser never built any more and nobody ever built one like theirs.

In development work with other companies it's always a bit of a risk and a problem. We had more than one-hundred people in our engineering department at one time and many of those fellas had ideas; they'd say why don't we try this. Meanwhile you had a customer who was "threatening" to buy a bunch of these things from you as part of a development deal. You're more inclined to do that development work with the customer. I always said we weren't the smartest people in the world, but we were smart enough to recognize the developments of others and if we couldn't develop something ourselves we hoped we could acquire a license or right from those who did.

In a development project somewhere someone has to make a decision as to whether you have an opportunity for success or whether you're going down the road of failure. Once I owned Coe it always fell on my shoulders to say let's get on or get off. To make a logical decision, you'd have to be very close to the development process to understand what's going on so that you can make the decision as to whether to go ahead and spend more money or just junk it and forget about it. We were always in the process of trying to make those decisions. When I left the company in 2000 we had twenty-two significant development projects in process from some close to maturity and some were just ideas and sketches on a piece of paper.

We had failures. Every technology company does. Our chief engineer came from FMC Corporation and he was asked once in a court hearing, what sort of success rate did you have in developments when you were with FMC's research and development department. And his response was if we were able to realize a ten percent success rate we were doing very well. He said here at Coe we're expecting ninety percent. He was a very bright guy and I respected his comment. I was never one to dwell on what I wish I had done or if had I done that. There were some things we spent quite a bit of money on; even though we had some success it may have been modest success that we would have been better advised to spend our time and money on something else. The veneer stitcher that I referred to earlier comes to mind.

Another real leap forward in the 1970s was the Model 72 dryer. This still involved the jet drying principle of the Model 62 dryer, but it had a larger, more efficient air system, and it corrected deficiencies of past dryers. Drying times were decreased some ten to fifteen percent. A new design of jet nozzle box was designed for the Model 72, and it was soon discovered that approximately the same design of a nozzle could be used as a retrofit in the Model 62 dryers, thereby increasing capacity by about five percent without making any other changes. Many thousand replacement nozzles were supplied on exactly this basis.

Another major acquisition occurred in 1974 when Coe purchased the assets of its longtime export agents, United States Machinery Company and United States Wallboard Machinery Company of New York City. Donald MacHarg who was the president and eight other executives and sales engineers moved to Painesville, which required another office extension by Coe. These companies represented other companies in kindred businesses throughout the world, and Coe acquired these sales territories as USM's subagents in various countries became agents of Coe. USM had orders for machinery for two large plywood plants in the Philippines, and these orders were transferred in their entirety to Coe. Voluminous records covering some fifty years of worldwide transactions were moved to the main office in Painesville.

In the ensuing couple of years, considerable plywood machinery business was transacted with Mexico and one large plasterboard plant was installed in Argentina. After about 1975, other than for the sale of parts, the export business tapered off. Competition grew and unfavorable exchange rates made foreign sales much more difficult, if not impossible. There was, however, much flurry about the possibility of selling ten plywood plants in one package to Russia, but after two or three fruitless trips to the Soviet Union by Coe sales officials, it was decided to give up on this prospect and to direct efforts elsewhere.

Although it did not seem to be of great importance compared to other happenings in 1974, Coe tore down two of the old mill buildings it had acquired in 1940 and replaced them with well designed storage, receiving and shipping facilities. This comprised some 12,000 square feet, and it included excellent facilities for crating and shipping export as well as domestic goods.

CHAPTER FIFTEEN

THE X-Y LATHE CHARGER

The X-Y computerized lathe charger was a wonderful development, not only for the success of Coe, but for the softwood plywood industry in the 1970s and 1980s. These devices improved veneer recovery on logs up to twenty percent. They made a dramatic contribution to the bottom line for plywood producers. For many plants, the computerized lathe charger was the difference between survival and closing.

In the mid 1970s we entered an agreement with Potlatch Corporation to develop a computerized charger, and thousands of hours later the first one began operation in 1977 at their plant in Lewiston, Idaho. It utilized two basic scanning concepts, the idea of blocked light, camera scanning and the idea of log rotation to get scan data. It basically worked like this: A log block was brought up to the jack ladder and centered in the pre-centering mechanical or geometric charger. It was then transferred to a set of charger spindles where it was chucked and rotated in the field of view of five cameras looking up at the shadow it cast from a light bar located above. The computer took this log shape and measurement data and very quickly calculated the optimum centerline of the block, which would yield the most full sheets of veneer. The positioning system then oriented each charger spindle in the X and Y direction so that when the block was picked up and delivered to the lathe by the charger arms, the optimum centerline of the block was at the centerline of the spindles, as the knife began peeling off the ribbon of veneer.

This was Coe's design, not my design, as we had a group of people who designed it. We also knew that it probably infringed on a patent that Fred Sohn had at his company Sun Studs in Roseburg. It was decided between Potlatch and ourselves that we would go ahead and build the machine and I told Potlatch that we, Coe, would make arrangements with Fred Sohn so that Potlatch and Coe wouldn't be charged with infringement. That's the way it went. It took me a couple of years but I eventually got a signed agreement with Sun Studs. They had developed this charging mechanism for their sawmill and they also had filed a patent application for use in a veneer mill, but it wasn't being used in a veneer mill. So I wanted to get the right to use their patents for veneer and plywood. They granted us the license for the plywood end of things.

Later on, Sun Studs built a veneer mill and they built an X-Y charger of their own and they had a very complicated scanning arrangement. Fred Sohn thought it was much better than what we had done. We said, well, if you have some friends who want to buy one, we'll be glad to build it and pay you royalty. He said okay and he said it was worth two and a half million dollars, which was about four times as much as ours. It may have been a quarter of one percent better in performance than ours, but you couldn't justify another two million dollars for it and we didn't do business together on that.

But going back to our computerized lathe charger, the license for which Fred Sohn granted to us in exchange for us paying him royalties when we would sell one—that agreement between us ran into some difficulty. In addition to a patent for use in a ply-wood mill, Fred Sohn along with a consultant named Carl Mason had filed patents for this very innovative computerized scanning, log charging and positioning sequence for a sawmill, where they actually planned to implement it first. But Fred still needed the computer software for the sawmill apparatus and he found someone through Oregon State in Corvallis who could write the software and do the computer programming. Fred met this programmer and showed him around the Sun Studs sawmill in Roseburg and explained to him what they were trying to do. Fred asked him if he could write a program and the fella said yes and went back to Corvallis. They apparently agreed that all the inventions and patents would remain the property of Sun Studs and the programmer will have been paid in full for his work.

Well they put this technology into the sawmill and it proved to be quite successful. Of course rumors run pretty wild in the wood business and U.S. Plywood had a plant just across town and Bill Whelan was vice president of U.S. Plywood in those days, and Bill and his people heard of this development in the sawmill. U.S. Plywood had a sawmill at McCloud River Lumber in McCloud, California and Bill Whelan said if this technology is doing that well, we ought to get one for our mill. So they went to the programmer and asked him if he could do the software for them and apparently he said he could. So they've built the plant at McCloud and it went into operation. Mr. Sohn is madder than hell when he hears about it because he thinks the programmer has violated their agreements and Mr. Sohn starts a lawsuit against this programmer's company for patent infringement, breach of contract and misappropriation of trade secrets, and the programmer counterclaims that Sun Studs' patents were invalid. The programmer company was soon purchased by another company, which assumed the lawsuit against the programmer.

In the meantime we had built and sold eight or ten of these computerized lathe chargers for the plywood industry and had paid Fred Sohn probably a hundred thousand dollars. But after a while he starts thinking about it, that he's fed up with all this lawsuit business and that maybe he stands to benefit by giving the license rights for use in a sawmill and plywood mill to the company who had purchased the programmer's company, the very company Fred Sohn is suing at the moment, the company that says Fred Sohn owes them money in royalties. So Mr. Sohn called me one day and says, Fred, I'm going to have to cancel our agreement. I'm going to turn the whole thing, lumber and plywood licensing, over to them. I said, wait, let's do some talking about this. He said I thought you might want to; my wife and I are coming to Portland, why don't we get together for lunch at the Benson Hotel in the Trader Vicks dining room and we can talk about this. We met there, including his attorney, and Mr. Sohn says to me, Fred, all I'm doing right now is paying out everything you're paying me in attorney's fees and I have nothing to show for it. I said, we're doing fairly well and we're paying you some money. He said we appreciate that but I'm getting fed up with fighting this damn lawsuit. I don't want to mess around with a patent suit the rest of my life. I've got a business to run. I'm up in years. My system won't take it. It's tearing me up. He looked at his attorney and said the attorney had read our agreement and the attorney had said Fred Sohn could cancel our agreement if it serves to settle in an expeditious way a dispute he might have. The attorney nodded and said that's right. I had gotten out the agreement beforehand and read it pretty closely as well, and I said, yes, it's right, excepting, where the agreement says you can cancel this only if it is reasonable. I said, Fred, it's not reasonable, and I'm telling you now if you want to cancel it, I'm going to sue you and you're going to have to fight me instead of these other people. He looks at his attorney and his wife is pale in the face, and he asks his lawyer if I'm right. I take out my copy of the agreement and point to where it says it at the bottom of one of the pages. The attorney reads it over, looks up at Fred Sohn and says, Fred's right, meaning me. Then Fred Sohn says, well, then I guess we don't cancel the agreement. And if you'll take over the suit then you don't have to pay me any more royalties. That's what we did. This remained in the courts for a number of years, until the late 80s, when a U.S. Court of Appeals for the Federal Court ruled that the other company had to halt the manufacture and sale of this equipment technology. In effect it accomplished what we were going after, which was to protect us and give us a proprietary position in selling X-Y chargers and protecting the patents that Fred Sohn and his organization had put together.

Patents can be useful and can provide some protection, but there are two sides to the coin. If you have a good idea and you decide not to apply for a patent, maybe you think it's too simple, or it's not patentable and you get it out on the market and you have a competitor that's always giving you a bad time and copying your ideas; they develop the same thing, they apply for the patent, you're cut off. You have no more rights even though it's your idea. If you don't protect yourself, somebody else can take that position and create a problem for you. At the same time, it costs a lot of money to go through the process of getting a patent. Sometimes you apply for a patent, you issue it to the patent office and they turn it down and the patent attorney says if you change this or change that I think they'll allow it. So you do this and that, spend more money, send it to the patent office and they turn it down again. After a while you begin to wonder if you're working for the patent office or for the attorney. The attorneys over the years have learned how to charge pretty well for that type of thing. We didn't have a so-called patents expert on staff at Coe, but we had a law firm in Portland and one in Cleveland. When I sold the company, we had a list of 175 patents. Sometimes we'd put the name of one our people on the patent who maybe wasn't the most involved with it, but we did that to make them feel good about their work and feel involved. If your well being depends on protecting what you think is right, that's the reason for spending money on patents. It's a difficult question, when do you get on and when do you get off? All of those matters of innovations and developments that relate to customers and employees and patent applications involve a lot of speculation. It costs money and if you back a bad horse it costs you a lot more money and you don't get anything out of it. But if you do something right, it's kind of like winning the lottery.

When we built the lathe chargers for Potlatch we used Redcon cameras. They could measure the dimension of a log but not very well. They weren't very accurate from a long range. They were accurate within several inches but when you get logs moving around you have to space the measuring device four or five feet away to keep them from getting hit with flying debris or steam from the logs which can fog up the camera lens. After Potlatch got the first one running, they wanted number two and number three. Potlatch had standardized in their plants with all IBM System 3 computers so they said to us, you build all the devices and tell us everything about how it operates and we'll write the software program for IBM System 3.

We started building those chargers right in the depth of the recession we had in those days and it really did a lot for the company because we could prove that they could get their money back in a year just in wood savings alone. We were selling them at a very good mark up and the customers were happy as hell. Even though the market was bad, the rewards were good and if a company was committed to staying in business a long period of time, they didn't mind spending the money. Kenneth Ford at Roseburg bought five of these camera-based X-Y lathe chargers. After we put the first one in at Potlatch, we told Kenneth what we had done and how it was working. We got on his airplane and went over to the Potlatch mill and took a look at it. He could realize what we were doing. He said he wanted to buy five. We're talking about seven-hundred or eight-hundred thousand dollars apiece. We proceed to have a lot of discussion about something he didn't know a darn thing about and I didn't know much more excepting I'd lived through the development of this first one we had built for Potlatch. We built his five and they were overwhelmingly successful and improved their recovery on logs by about twenty percent and each of them paid for themselves in less than a year.

Now John Nosler was a guy who lived in Eugene and he had

worked up a laser scanner with triangulation means of determining distance and measurements for Fred Sohn in scanning logs for the sawmill and for the lathe charger in Fred's plywood mill. John had developed this scanner which would enable long range scanning of logs, like ten to twenty feet, with a great deal of accuracy. It was designed to get precise, accurate log shape data at many points around the log with which to optimize the positioning and charging of that log into a lathe.

Like I said, the computerized chargers we had been installing used Redcon cameras and we recognized the fact the camera was not very accurate and meanwhile our engineering people were very impressed with Nosler's laser scanner. I didn't know anything about the laser scanner, not many people did in our business. But Nosler came to our chief engineer and said I'm not cut out for this type of work. I think it's a good device but I can't stand working with these manufacturing people. I become very deep in thought in developing something and some mechanic comes along and says he can't get the screw in the hole and it just drives me up the creek. Nosler was a bright guy and a nice fella. He wasn't a kook, he was just that way. The first time our chief engineer, Art McGee, and I took a trip with him, he was making scanners for measuring the thickness of cookie dough and we went to Keebler's cookie plant in Cincinnati to see an installation. I was in Painesville so I flew down to Cincinnati and Art McGee and John Nosler flew from Portland. When they checked into the hotel where I was staying, Nosler made the comment to Art that he couldn't stand to sleep alone. He was bothered by that. There they were, so they got a room with two single beds and everything worked out fine. Apparently he was one of those fellas who had always traveled with his wife and he was just frightened to death of being alone and of sleeping alone. We got through that one. He was somewhat the same in business. He had this shop and he made these devices. He was educated as a physicist, probably in his 30s. Fred Sohn had heard about and told him what he wanted and Nosler had said sure I can do that and he worked up this laser scanner. And it was successful. We recognized it was successful. And he could go see our scanners and knew that what he had was better than ours. So he came to us and said he would like to sell the device and individual unit, and we said we were interested and then he got more serious and wanted to sell his whole business. The first thing we asked was, is this yours or Fred Sohn's. He said, oh no, this is mine, it has nothing to do with Fred Sohn and he eventually got patent protection on it. Over the years we paid him a very handsome sum of money because the scanner was a significant success and we used it in a lot of applications. The laser scanner was not only used for the X-Y chargers in plywood mills and in sawmills, but it was used for positioning the core drive and other devices used in and around the veneer lathe and also used in detecting defects in veneer in the green form and defects in the panel form after it had been laid up and glued together. We made a deal with Nosler, negotiated a contract with him where we paid him a percentage of the sale price and I think we paid him a million dollars and that was what he was looking for. He would say I want a million dollars. So through that process we bought the company in 1982. We bought his shop facilities and moved them to Portland where we made the scanners in our own shop. Nosler went on to develop other things. He was an unusual guy, a very smart guy and a good friend. He's no longer alive.

We had installed perhaps one-hundred computerized chargers utilizing blocked light, camera scanning before we implemented Nosler's laser scanner, which was also referred to as the Image Displacement Scanner. Basically the Nosler scanner shined a laser beam on the log block to determine the distance of that object from the scanner. The laser light was reflected off the block in all directions, with some of the light reflected back toward the scanner. That light was gathered by a lens and focused on an array. A microprocessor and associated electronics discerned the location of the laser dot on the array and used that information to calculate the distance of the block from the scanner. As the block moved in relation to the scanner, the laser dot was focused on a different location of the array. When correlated with the information from other sources about the block's location and movement relative to the scanner, this information allowed the determination of the block's shape as well as distance from the scanner. The laser's intensity enabled the laser scanner to be used on log blocks varying in reflectivity from black to white. Thus the laser's use eliminated one of the early problems associated with reflected light scanning. The blocked light, camera scanning worked particularly well in the case of uniform logs, but had its drawbacks for misshapen logs in that the shadow of the log is somewhat different than its actual shape. The laser scanner on the other hand could measure directly along the radial for which the measurement is recorded. It could see the dips in the log's surface that the blocked light scanner was unable to see. In addition to giving a truer picture of the log's shape, the laser scanner also had higher resolution than the blocked light camera type scanner. There were five of these scanners on eight foot lathe machines and seven scanners on a ten foot machine. Another major benefit of the laser scanner was its ability to run properly with little attention, compared to the camera scanners which had to be cleaned by the mill personnel, and typically if one or two of the cameras were covered in debris, they wouldn't be cleaned until the end of the shift, and you can start counting the number of logs that would be improperly scanned until the end of the shift. The laser scanners were mounted above the log in an area where they were protected and easily kept clean.

There were quite a few changes as we went along, not only in the charging and peeling machinery, but with all of our products. You always learn something different in every machine you build. The tendency is to keep improving upon it. Sometimes that aggravated somebody like myself who was trying to run a business and make some money, and the damn engineers kept changing things.

CHAPTER SIXTEEN

WHY DON'T YOU BUY COE?

I never gave much thought to leaving Coe for another position. I had too much blood, sweat and tear in what I was doing. I was never unhappy at Coe. Coe had treated me almost as if I was a son. My tax attorney once said to me that Frank Milbourn, Jr. has probably treated me better than he treated his two sons. I said I didn't think so. But Coe was a very sound organization and they treated me as well as I could have expected and so I had no reason to do anything other than to try to enhance the business of Coe and that was my state of mind the day Frank Milbourn, Jr. told me he was selling the business. I was absolutely dumbfounded. I thought simply that the two sons, Frank III and George, were going to take over and run the business. Both were in their 30s and had worked in the company since they were teenagers. Both had been with the company full time since their respective graduations from Vanderbilt and Dennison universities. The night Mr. Milbourn told me, we were in Minneapolis and he took me to his hotel room and told me he was going to sell the company and I said oh you can't mean it. He said yes I really do. I said well would you permit me to talk to your two sons. I'll happily volunteer and run the business for them for four or five years until they get a handle on it if they're looking for someone to do that. They shouldn't be selling this business. That's how dedicated I felt to the family and the business. Mr. Milbourn said I know, I've tried to talk them out of it for six months now. Neither son had majored in engineering and they reasoned that they were not engineers and that the company was becoming more and more engineering oriented. And they wanted to diversify their careers somewhat.

I tried to talk the two boys out of it. They had a sister involved who was a shareholder, too. They told me they had talked about it for over a year and they appreciated everything their dad and granddad had done for them but they didn't feel that they were capable of running the business. I offered to run it for them for a few years until they got a handle on it but they wanted to find something else that was more suited to their intellect and ambitions. In other words, they didn't change their minds.

Mr. Milbourn told me there was a company in Cleveland that was interested in buying Coe called Midland Ross Company. They were heavy into the industrial machinery business and had many different divisions. They asked Mr. Milbourn whom he would suggest that they could meet with about running the operation and Mr. Milbourn offered my name. I met with them in Cleveland and also in Portland and I decided well if this is going to happen maybe I should cooperate in every way I could and see if I couldn't make the best of it. We talked and talked and nobody was involved in the discussion except the Milbourns and myself, and all of the sudden one day Mr. Milbourn called and said Midland Ross decided they had two companies in New Jersey who made electrical fasteners that were losing money hand over fist and the chairman said they were not going to buy anything, including Coe, as long as they were losing money in those plants. Harry Bowell was the chairman. I didn't know him very well, but I did know him and I think he was probably making a good decision. They asked if they could come back in six months and renegotiate and reestablish their plan of a letter of intent and Mr. Milbourn told them that would be fine but his major objective was to sell the company and he wasn't going to wait for them, but if he hadn't sold it in six months that he would entertain continued negotiations.

A month or so later Mr. Milbourn called me and said a company in Philadelphia was interested in buying and it was a company called Proctor Schwartz. I knew the company and I thought they made a lot of junkie or inferior equipment and I told Mr. Milbourn this and that I wouldn't feel good about working for them. He said they have the money and they're a good company and they've been in business for fifty years or so. I said if I worked for them and was successful I might get a pat on the back. If I wasn't successful I'd get fired and the odds were things wouldn't work out very well. So one day Mr. Milbourn called and said these fellas are coming over here with a letter of intent and they're going to be here next week. I said I don't know what I can say to you but I still don't think too well of them. He said, "Well, why don't you buy the company?" I said, "Frank, I don't have any money." He said well you can go to your friends down at the bank and you can borrow some money. I said I don't know about that. He said why don't you just take a look at it, I'll send you all the financial details, which he did.

At that time the market was in a recession, at least the plywood market was in a recession. The sales at Coe in 1976 had dropped from $18 million to $12 million. I guess I was blind to the possibility that maybe the economy would never come back. I always felt strongly about the potential of the plywood business. It had had its ups and downs since World War II, some of them serious. Recently there had been an extensive study made of the markets. That report was fairly favorable in 1975, and I had had the benefit of studying that report pretty well and I agreed with it and I'm not sure if some of the information that was used they didn't get indirectly from me. It was done by Sandwell Engineering, a large

engineering company in Vancouver. They did have a good knowledge of the plywood business and I'm sure they used other
sources that were familiar with the plywood industry. At that time
I had lived with the industry for thirty years, and the softwood plywood business had gotten a good running start. It hadn't hit its
peak yet. It wasn't long after that, that it hits its peak. Outside of
Johnny Martin's plant that he built in the mid-1990s in Louisiana,
the last softwood plywood plant had been built in about 1982, the
Boise plant at Chester, South Carolina and maybe the Georgia-
Pacific plant at Hawthorne, Florida. But in the 1970s, as I was
contemplating the purchase of Coe, the plywood industry was
really just getting into the most modern technology. We were
doing a lot of research and development work particularly related
to the X-Y lathe chargers and about to put the first ones in, and the
core drive came along after that and other things related to peeling
techniques that really made a significant difference. The industry
was pointing toward peeling smaller diameter logs, which hadn't
been done much before, and though it was difficult to get a good
volume of production out of small logs, it was still economical.
The industry was hammering away and moving in the direction of
better recovery from smaller logs and lower cost logs. So I felt I
had a pretty good understanding of the situation. But there still
was a lot of anxiety when I signed the documents to buy Coe.

At that time a very good friend of mine was executive vice
president of West Coast operations of Merrill Lynch. He was in
town and so on a Saturday morning I took him down to the
office of our auditor and accountant, Garthe Brown, and they
convinced me I knew more about the business than most anybody and I should be buying it. I said well I've got to have some
money. They said call up your banker friend. I did know the
chairman of U.S. Bank in Portland, John Elorriga. He had been
the previous president of Evans Products and I knew him at that
position. Brown and I went down and visited with him one afternoon and showed him the financial statements. John didn't say
too much, just turned around and picked up the phone and said
I'm going to get one of our vice presidents in here, which he did

and he told this fella, Harris Rosendahl, he said you get a ticket to Cleveland, Ohio and go back with these guys to Painesville and buy Coe Company and you give Fred whatever money he needs. I borrowed one-hundred cents on the dollar. I had a few dollars and I had to sign that over to the bank with some stock certificates. I borrowed all the money and needless to say I was about as nervous as anyone could be. A month before it had never entered my mind. John said now Fred if you want a partner I'll go with you. I said, John, I'd love to have you as a partner, but if I fail and I have a partner, I will be looking for the tallest bridge in town to jump off of. If I'm successful it's fine, but if I fail I don't want to be obligated to somebody else and cause someone else to lose money. I'm either going to do it myself or I don't want to do it at all. I just bowed my neck and said I guess I better go to work. That was in December 1976.

I had confidence that I could do this. Being out here in Portland, the Milbourns had let me do what I chose to do. We generated half of the company's profits, half the company's business. I had gained a lot of experience from 1947 to 1977 with Coe. I had just turned 54 years old. I had had a good experience and probably a better experience in the industry than anyone in Painesville. And in the meantime I commuted to Ohio fairly frequently and I was familiar with their manufacturing and costs and engineering. But confidence or no confidence, there were great moments of anxiety. One of the largest law firms in the country was in Cleveland and they were handling my transaction with Mr. Milbourn. I always remember we negotiated all the important issues and the question got down to what kind of interest do you pay, do you want variable interest or do you want a fixed interest rate. I marched up and down their hall. I think I wore out their carpeting on that one floor of the office worrying about that. I said okay we're going to take a nine percent fixed interest rate. And Rosendahl the vice president of the bank said that's just fine. And so after that the interest rates went to seventeen percent.

My wife was a little bit curious about it. I usually talked to

Frank Milbourn on the phone around six to seven o'clock from home and she always heard the conversations. And during these particular conversations her eyes would roll and she said why in the world do you want to do that, you have everything you need and more. What more do you want? I said well I'm like the old farmer, you live on the farm all your life and finally get the mortgage paid off and the first thing you want to do is buy your neighbor's farm. I guess that's a little bit of the same situation.

Mr. Milbourn had been willing to help his sons every step of the way if they had purchased the company. When I bought it, he did the same for me. He helped me every day. He was a fantastic fella. He was just as generous as he could be. He gave my wife a lot of confidence, too. They got along fine. She would come into the office and sit and talk to him for hours. He was a good story teller and a good level head. I saw the oldest boy some time ago down in the desert and he said you know the best thing that ever happened to Coe Company was when Fred bought it. That was a nice comment to make. Frank the third bought a travel agency. George, the younger son, is now the chairman of the Martha Holden Jennings Foundation, which is an Ohio foundation that provides funds for secondary education and to encourage educators to better themselves through additional study. George is a good, smart fella. He was our sales manager. Both of them continued to work for me after I bought the company for several years.

No one had gotten wind of the deal until after all the smoke had cleared away. I came out to Painesville and made the announcement with Mr. Milbourn. It was a good transition. We had to get our financial affairs in order, sort of a laborious task. No real surprises, except for one. About a month later I walked into the office in Painesville and Mr. Milbourn said I forgot to tell you, I went back to the vault—we had a big vault that extended over three floors, the basement, the main floor and the second floor—and I forgot that I had an envelope back there, here's the envelope, there's 10,000 dollars in one hundred dollar bills there. I said really. He said that belongs to you, that's the company's money, you bought the company, it's yours. We had sold a machine down in Brazil and after a recession hit Brazil the guy down there wanted to cancel the order. We didn't want to cancel because we had quite a bit of it built. They agreed on a split. He gave the salesman from Coe back ten thousand dollars in one-hundred dollar bills. The salesman wasn't supposed to bring that amount of money back into the United States. He brought it in anyway and Mr. Milbourn said how did you get through customs with that. He said I just walked through. Did they ask you if you had any money? He said no they didn't ask. So Mr. Milbourn was afraid to spend it. But that had been 10 years prior to that. He was afraid they had all those hundred dollar bills numbered. After he gave it to me, I put it in my safety deposit box and when I ran out of money I pulled out a hundred dollar bill and I used them one at a time.

My wife and I found a place in Painesville right away. I bought the company in December and it was effective the first of the year, 1977. By the fifth of January Sue and I had rented a house and the first week it snowed thirty inches and was thirty below zero. I have a picture of the house and Sue standing in front of it with that thirty inches of snow. I finally bought a house later on that was fairly close to the office and kept it until I left the company in 2000.

Like I said, in 1977, about the time I bought Coe Company, business was starting to slow down. But we were well into developing the X-Y lathe charger and we put the first one in at Potlatch shortly thereafter and it became an immediate success, and continued to be a success as we improved the scanning on it with laser scanning from Nosler, which as I also stated earlier we eventually purchased. So even though the economy was down, there were companies like Roseburg and others who felt that if you're going to stay in business you better look like it and you better get your plant modernized to compete the best way you know how. If you're not going to stay business and you can't afford it, then don't spend any money, but those that could like the Weyerhaeusers, the G-Ps and the Fords, here came the X-Y charger that was generating something like 20 percent improvement in recovery and they couldn't afford not to have it. I took a lesson from that. We tried to do our development work when business was good and when business wasn't so good we'd go out and try to sell these new innovations that a person or company could realize a return on their money in 18 months to two years. Business was slow, these companies didn't have a lot of work to do, so they saw it as a good time to modernize their plants. As a result Coe had good sales and we didn't have to lay anybody off in those days or at least not very many.

I suppose my management style was a little bit different than the previous owner. Somebody once wrote that I ran the company as a dictator. I never saw like it like that. I'm sure some of the employees didn't like me or my style. We would have production meetings and I would insist on some answers and asked in some ways people took offense to, but we worked our way through those problems. I asked them to do things a little differently, sometimes they didn't like it. But if you're betting your own money on whatever you're doing, which I now was, whether you're betting on horses or betting on the success of your engineering people, somebody has to make a decision. At larger corporations such as a Weyerhaeuser, sometimes those decisions are made by committee. At smaller companies like Coe, it comes down to one person. I talked a little bit earlier about the touchy situations that could arise as a result of development projects with customers or whether to develop the original ideas of your own engineering people, and the possible hurt feelings or lost business that could come out of it. We had three or four key guys in the company, and the engineering group and the sales group would put their heads together. Maybe I didn't make all the decisions, but whether it was Ralph Gage or Gene Knokey or Art McGee, whoever it was doesn't make any difference, the guy who gets blamed for it is me. I got to the point where I sort of brushed it off my shoulder and went down the road and did the best I possibly could. Frankly we had some darn good guys at Coe; they were good thinkers—our engineering people, our service people, all of whom contributed to the ideas and to those things that were required to become successful. I wasn't the only guy in the company, but from the outside that's probably how it looked at times. How would I grade myself as a manager or organizer? I'd say I was fair.

Before I purchased Coe, I had never really owed any money. I had bought an automobile or two when I was younger on credit, but I never borrowed money like I did when I bought Coe Company. I wasn't nervous, but I was anxious to get that loan paid off. I did everything I could in the way of saving money and reducing costs and made all efforts to get the loan paid off. I had a five year loan with a balloon payment at the end of five years. Each year I made my minimum payment plus whatever I could muster to reduce my payments and reduce my debt and the banks recognized that as good faith on my part. I told them that if tough times came along I might not be able to make my payments, but I wanted to get ahead of the game to support the lean times. I ended up paying it off in three and a half years. In addition to the immediate success we had with the X-Y lathe charger, there was something else that helped out considerably.

The Milbourns had run the business since 1919. I don't know what they paid for it, but it was a minimal amount. I'm sure they kept investing in the buildings and tools and so forth. Like every company, you make pretty good money one year and the next year you don't do as well. During that entire period from when they started to when I bought it, I think it was 1932 that they lost $420. That was the only year that they had a loss. When I bought the company in late 1976, prior to that there was a 531 code in the tax law that covered companies such as Coe that had an undue accumulation of cash. In other words, if you had a certain percentage of money that was in cash, and maybe you had it in bonds or other investments, you had to pay it out in dividends so the government would get the tax on the dividend. Rather than pay it out in dividends, the Milbourns invested in inventory of raw materials. When I bought the company they had a very substantial inventory of sheet metal and steel of varying descriptions and some of that had been in the warehouse for four or five years. When I bought the company, that material had been written off the books, so I realized the benefit of that. The first couple of years that I ran Coe Company, the policy I established was we don't buy anymore steel or sheet metal until we have reduced that inventory to practically nothing. We built a lot of dryers in those days and the sheet metal used in those dryers came at a very minimal cost which helped me greatly in generating profits. I've got to give the previous regime at Coe the credit for making it a little easier. Had we not had good technology and had we not had an improved economy, we wouldn't have had the business and I wouldn't have been able to reduce that steel inventory and reduce my debt; the rub of the green as they say on the golf course.

Another thing that helped us was getting into the manufacturing of automated layup lines. I talked before about how Weyerhaeuser built one and we had an agreement with them, but that Georgia-Pacific came out with a better layup line and we were left holding the bag for just a while. After we had built our plant in Tigard, Oregon, Georgia-Pacific bought about seven acres of property adjacent to us and built a manufacturing facility, about 75,000 square feet. They brought a lot of used machinery into that shop out of pulp and paper mills and they'd refurbish it and use it as replacement parts for their operating mills, but I always viewed it as kind of a play thing for the executives of G-P. Then in the early 80s they decided to move their headquarters from downtown Portland to downtown Atlanta and they left the plant as an orphan with no one to oversee it. They decided to sell it and we bought the land and the buildings and we also got the right to build the G-P layup system as part of the deal.

And so it all came together pretty nicely, and a lot of softwood plywood plants installed the latest technologies and would continue to do so for years to come. But the building of new softwood plywood mills was on the wane, and Coe needed to diversify its technologies in other directions. Around 1980 there were 170 plywood plants and by comparison there were about 1,200 sawmills and we were looking at those markets as being important to us. We were having good success with our X-Y chargers and our scanners and positioners and we felt the logical direction was to use that same higher level of technology in the sawmills, whether it be at the headrig or edger or trimmer or wherever. As I discussed earlier I purchased Nosler Scanner in 1982, whose applications we used initially in the plywood mills, but were applicable for sawmills as well. This scanning apparatus permitted us to measure the configuration of logs and to get a histogram if you will, to get an exact precise diameter and length. In doing so, the computer then could crunch the numbers and determine the best profile for us to either peel those logs or break them up into lumber sections that had the best profitability. I felt very positive about getting into the lumber business. It seemed that the plywood end had grown to a mature state and we felt that the saturation point of that type of equipment was going to come relatively fast and it was time to move on and begin doing some other things.

CHAPTER SEVENTEEN

ACQUISITION BINGE

My next purchase got us into the sawmill business pretty quickly. In 1982 I bought the old Moore Dry Kiln Company. They were on the verge of bankruptcy frankly and they came to us wanting to sell the business. We were competing with them for veneer dryers and board dryers for gypsum board and fiberboard. That business was very competitive and it just got one more competitor out of the picture if you will. Moore Dry Kiln Company had a rich history, with roots going back to the late 1800s in Jacksonville, Florida. It was named for its founder, Lafayette Moore. They sold dry kilns throughout the South, and then the company expanded into the Northwest and formed Moore Dry Kiln Company of Oregon in 1927. There were Moore dry kilns at sawmills all over this country and then at the beginning of World War II they installed roller veneer dryers and became a competitor of Coe in that regard.

So we bought Moore and along with it we got Morvue Electronics, which made veneer clipper scanners, and we got Moore Canada, Moore Memphis and a group of Moore companies. The Portland business built dryers and kilns, Canada made kilns, Memphis built dry kilns. Its Klamath Iron Works group built headrigs and carriages for sawmills. We didn't do what we thought we could do in the lumber business at that time as quickly as we might have. It took quite a bit of development to adopt scanning and positioning and so forth for things like a headrig or an edger or trimmer. It took us several years to develop that and we were successful in getting it done but in the meantime other people were moving ahead as well and probably a little faster than we were. After the acquisition, all the managers of the various Moore plants joined the Coe organization, as did several of its engineers and sales personnel. That was our initial start in getting back into the sawmill business. If you'll recall, Coe had been in the sawmill business at the turn of the century before getting into the plywood business. It worked out because we now had the extra manufacturing space at Tigard, having bought the G-P facility, and when we acquired Moore we moved the Moore Oregon operations into that building.

Moore was my third significant acquisition since taking over Coe, following G-P's manufacturing facility and Nosler Scanner. Our next acquisition, in 1984, provided the transition we needed into the emerging composite panel business. Like Moore, it was a company with a long history.

Washington Iron Works was officially organized in 1882 in Seattle, Washington, though its founders previously operated Tenny & Frink, an iron and brass foundry business. John Frink had been raised in the Northeast, but gradually migrated west by way of the dusty farmlands of Kansas before selling his farm and venturing to San Francisco and then Seattle, where he first worked as a day laborer, digging wells and doing any physical labor he could find to support himself. He then became a school teacher and principal in Belltown and Port Gamble. It was in Port Gamble where he met L.H. Tenny, who was in the business of supplying foundry castings to the area's sawmills. Frink became enamored of the business and the twosome formed a partnership and moved to Seattle and opened Tenny & Frink. Apparently they did well from the outset because it wasn't long before Frank traveled to Portland and purchased thirty tons of machinery from a failing company called Columbia Iron Works. The equipment was transported via steamer to Seattle and shortly after, in January 1882, the partners formed Washington Iron Works.

The company's forte became steam engines for sawmills and steam donkeys for logging operations while continuing to make steel castings. The business was passed down to John Frink's son, Gerald, and after World War I introduced its first diesel engine, which became its primary product and it also manufactured logging yarders for the Northwest timber industry. Business during World War II was good with the production of huge steel castings for building cargo ships and carriers, and smaller castings for the B-29 bomber. It also produced these large cranes, five and six stories tall with booms 100 to 150 feet long, and sold these to shipyards and for major dam projects.

It wasn't until the 1950s that the company began producing hydraulic presses, for the pulp industry initially, and this led to the manufacture of multi-opening presses for wood products, including composite board. The Frick family sold the business in 1971. One of the company's more interesting projects was a contract in 1981 to build a complete medium density fiberboard plant in the People's Republic of China. Just a couple of years later, in 1984, I bought Washington Iron Works and became immersed up to my ears in this China project.

When we bought Washington Iron Works they were being forced out of their manufacturing facilities in Seattle by the City. They were situated on a 12 acre site in downtown Seattle and the city wanted it for a transportation barn for city buses and streetcars. At that time the cost of shipping steel for heavy plates to go into an MDF or OSB press was something terrific. The only place the plates were made in one piece in the United States was in Coatsville, Pennsylvania near Philadelphia. So the cost of shipping those plates that weighed 70 to 90 thousand pounds apiece—and there would be fifteen of them in one press that required you ship them from Pennsylvania to Seattle and machine them into the configuration of the plate and drill them for steam passages and so forth and ship them back to a plant in Wisconsin or Maine or Quebec—was twice the cost of shipping a steel plate from say Hamburg, Germany to Maine, especially when you also figured in the exchange rate that was in favor of the German press manufacturers. So the German manufacturers were coming in and taking a market that had been dominated by Washington Iron Works, which was losing practically all the business because of freight. Another reason they were having trouble was because the plant in Seattle was built back in the 1890s and some of the equipment was terribly antiquated and it took them many more hours to manufacture something than a modern plant would.

The City bought the property, including the plant and the equipment, from the guy who owned it, Guy Martin. I bought the engineering drawings and the details that related to the manufacturing process. After the City bought it they auctioned off all the machine tools that they had, most of which were antiquated or obsolete, but there were a few special tools that were needed and I went to the sale and bought what I thought we ought to have as I had decided we were going to build a new plant for the Washington Iron Works business in Painesville. It would save us a lot on freight and save us a lot of time because we bought modern machinery to do our work and our labor rates in Ohio were about three dollars an hour less as compared to Seattle. The Seattle plant had been controlled labor rate wise by the Teamster's union who had the Longshoremen control anything that was fairly technical like machinists and aerospace workers and Boeing controlled the price of labor. By moving to Ohio, we would have a modern plant, much lower labor rates and cut our freight costs for heavy steel plates almost in half. For that reason I bought Washington Iron Works thinking that they had a good product line and that we could compete with the Germans and the Swedes, which we did. We had one year to move out of the

Seattle plant, so we were able to manufacture a few presses in Seattle before we had to get out.

But let me get back to the project in China that we inherited from Washington Iron Works. Nixon had gone to China and broken the ice during his presidency and as a result of that some years later the U.S. government invited mainland China to send some groups over to study various types of manufacturing. There were two study groups that pertained to our industry, maybe twelve to fifteen people in each, plant managers and so called engineers and technicians of various types, but they were not the type of technician we would think in terms of. But they came here to study the manufacturing means of softwood plywood, which they were not manufacturing very much of in those days. They manufactured hardwood plywood and Coe had supplied them with lathes and various types of veneer equipment to peel hardwood such as maple and birch and other hardwood species, but they had not done anything to speak of with softwood like pine and firs and so forth. So they sent these two groups to the United States, one to study the peeling and processing of plywood, the other to study composition board such as particleboard and oriented strandboard. They had been manufacturing products like Masonite product a number of years which I guess they had a license that started back before World War II. Masonite's products began back in the 20s and 30s by a fella the name of Mason down in Laurel, Mississippi. The Chinese were manufacturing Masonite but not particleboard, medium density fiberboard or oriented strandboard. They made arrangements through the state department to send each of the teams in the various directions to see the technologies. The government came to Coe and asked us to outline a tour of plants where these Chinese could see modern facilities producing softwood plywood. We put something together for them and we showed them around the Southern states and the West Coast. At the same time they sent a study group to Washington Iron Works, which also established a tour to various plants, primarily medium density fiberboard. After the Chinese had conducted these two studies and after many months of contemplation they finally decided they would buy a complete medium density fiberboard plant from Washington Iron Works. Mind you they had been peeling veneer and making plywood for a long time, even though it was hardwood, but they hadn't been doing much in the way of making MDF or particleboard and they thought they would do something they had very little knowledge of. They contracted with Washington Iron Works to build this turnkey MDF plant at Fujou, China on the Pacific Coast, probably 175 to 200 miles north of Hong Kong. They contracted to build that plant in 1981 and we bought Washington Iron Works in 1984. They had built the plant and the plant had been running maybe for a year when we bought Washington Iron Works.

In the process this plant in Fujou, China was up and running but the Chinese had refused to pay Washington Iron Works the last two million dollars that was owed on the project. They claimed it wasn't producing as was guaranteed and they weren't going to pay until it was. So the management of Washington Iron Works came to me and said you bought our company and hired all our engineering and technical people and we have this problem in China that you didn't inherit but we've got to have some help in getting that thing resolved or we're going to have to go to Stockholm and go to arbitration. I said I'll spend the money to go over and take a look and talk to the people if you'll send an interpreter and a couple of technicians to go with me and so the four of us went. The interpreter was a Chinese born engineer who was working for the City of Seattle. He was a very bright young person and a darn good interpreter. Before we went I had learned that one of the problems they had was that the boiler couldn't maintain steam pressure to keep the refining and the press and various things that require steam up to pressure and volume. The Washington Iron Works group said it was poor quality coal; it was a coal fired boiler. I hired an engineer from Pittsburgh who was an expert on coal and sent him over there two weeks in advance and told him to go over there make that damn boiler work on the coal that they have. When we arrived at

Fujou airport this engineer met me and said we really need to talk before we go meet with the principals of the plant, who were waiting to see me right away. The engineer said we need an hour or so before we do that. So we snuck off in a corner and talked for an hour and he said I went over there and took all the wooden crates and everything I could find that was combustible and I got the biggest fire going that I could possibly create and then started pouring this coal on top of it and as I started to pour the coal on, the fire started to go out. And he said Mr. Fields that coal was half rock. It was black but it wasn't coal. He said you open the boiler up and you'll find in the grates, the thing is loaded with rocks.

We sat down with the Chinese and we explained to them that Washington Iron Works didn't guarantee that it would burn rock. The reason they wanted to use this coal was that it was mined in the local area. It was anthrosite coal. The soft coal which would burn easily was located up in the north end of Manchuria and it cost them 40 dollars a ton to ship it down from Manchuria and they didn't want to pay that extra cost. I told them I could understand that but if the material won't burn…We argued for two or three days and I finally got the point across. Mind you they had been running the plant for almost two years. They did a terrible job of maintaining it, they had no one with any experience and they didn't have decent mechanics. The plant was really in shambles. They not only needed to use coal, but they had to get the plant back in decent repair. I went in and we looked at the plant and I had an electrician and a mechanic and this interpreter and we went in and surveyed the plant and decided we could supply all the spare parts that were needed to repair the equipment for maybe $350,000, which was a heavy hit. I made a deal with them that if they took care of the boiler problem—I didn't care how they took care of it, if they bought a new boiler, a local boiler and supplied the steam that was fine with me or used soft coal from Manchuria, whatever they wanted to do, you fix the boiler problem—then we'll fix the plant so that it'll operate properly as intended and do a better of training your people if you will pay us what you owe us. Washington Iron Works had agreed to let Coe Company have whatever we could collect from the project.

It took us about a year to get all the parts shipped, with all the shipping papers and complications and the engineering work and finally we got the plant to where it was in a decent state of repair. One thing they had that was always a problem was that the fire protection system wasn't very good and the fiber would catch on fire every once in a while and the whole damn plant would almost burn down. We had that occur several times. The problem was people. I would go into the plant at midnight and go to the operator's control room, and it was sort of a lunch room and it had four or five large tables in it, that's where the technicians would work and do their sampling of the product. I walked in there at night and all the operators are lying in there on those tables sound asleep. The only time they woke up was when the alarm rang and something broke down and by that time there was just hell to pay; all the air systems would be plugged up. I had to go to the management and lecture to them that we can't operate this way, you've got to make a plant run. That was a chore in itself. But we finally got it running. We probably put in $500,000 in parts and service and equipment and we collected almost all of the rest of the money that was owed us. It was quite an experience. I had decided that we wanted to do business with China and this would be an opportunity to find out just how tough it was to deal with the Chinese. Finishing a job is the most difficult part. Selling something, that's easy. Installing it and making things go is always the most difficult chore and we found that holy smokes you just can barely satisfy the Chinese and all their wants, desires and demands that they make in starting a plant of that kind.

We didn't pursue the Chinese business very much after that. We sold some veneer lathes over there. Later on we bid on another MDF plant but the German companies were bound and determined they were going to get the business. We had to put up a hundred thousand dollars just to bid. They just kept yanking us around one month after the other. I finally gave up. I said it takes the best people we have to do business with them and we're just ruining the rest of our business by devoting all of our time to trying to do business with the Chinese. If you're young and twenty-one and have the rest of your life to devote to it...

As for Russia, I made several trips over there along with some of our people and we saw a lot of our old equipment that was made back in the 1930s. The Fins had dominated that industry for years because they would simply trade them machinery for gold or oil or whatever. Russia did everything on a barter basis and we weren't a barter business, so we didn't do much business with them either.

The problem we had in dealing with the German press manufacturers had to do with the German government finance arm. Say the German manufacturer came to the United States and secured a five million dollar order; they took a ten percent downpayment, and they'd go back to Germany, go to the government and say we got the order and got ten percent of the money, and the government would say okay we'll give you your ten percent now and as you manufacture we'll give you progress payments and we'll finance it. And they'd carry the paper for five years at a low interest rate and so it wasn't the manufacturer doing the financing, it was the government. That generated work for employees and so it was good business for the country in general and that's the reason they got about sixty percent of their gross national product as export business.

A lot of people in this country would not buy their equipment because it wasn't Americanized with design and parts. It was manufactured to suit their own designs and standards and a lot of people in this country got tired of that; they couldn't maintain it or if it had flaws in it, or any number of problems and sometimes the German people would aggravate American people. It was just personalities that would create problems between the two. It certainly did help us.

CHAPTER EIGHTEEN

RIDING THE OSB WAVE

The Washington Iron Works business, our ability to develop it, caused Coe's sales revenue to take a major leap. In the early 1980s the cost of a Washington Iron Works multi-opening press was several million dollars. Louisiana-Pacific put WIW presses in at their first two oriented strandboard plants, in Hayward, Wisconsin and Houlton, Maine. However, that was in the late 1970s and early 1980s, before Coe bought Washington Iron Works.

I spoke earlier about Harry Merlo, the former Georgia-Pacific western executive who took charge of the properties G-P was forced to spin off in the early 1970s to relieve the pressure it was getting from the Federal Trade Commission, which had accused G-P of having a monopoly on southern pine plywood. The new company, led by Merlo, was called Louisiana-Pacific. After the spin-off, and in the ensuing years, Merlo aggressively added to Louisiana-Pacific's portfolio. He bought many sawmills, espe-

cially in the South, plywood plants, timberland, a medium density
fiberboard plant and continued buying. Then, as Merlo tells it, he
was attending a housing show in Dallas when he came upon a
sample of a composite board that was manufactured in Canada.
He checked out of his hotel and was soon on his plane visiting the
various Canadian manufacturers of this reconstituted board. At
that time, MacMillan Bloedel was making it at Hudson Bay and
Thunder Bay, Malotte at Timmins, Weldwood at Longlac,
Blandin at Grand Rapids and Weyerhaeuser was starting up a
plant in Slave Lake. Within thirty days, Merlo and Jim Eisses,
who was head of L-P's composite board development, had
ordered the equipment for their first plant to be built in Hayward.

Everybody who looked at this product thought it was a good
building product. Primarily it was inexpensive because they used
wood that wasn't good to use for anything else. They'd go up to
the northern parts of Wisconsin, Maine, Minnesota, Quebec,
Ontario, Manitoba and anywhere they could find big stands of
aspen and weed trees that would grow very fast. These trees
would grow for twenty to twenty-five years and if they weren't
cut they would die. If they died, the skeleton tree would just
stand there. If they were cut and harvested they'd re-grow. This
was the attraction. You could buy the aspen at very low prices at
the stump like you're buying weed trees. They were easy to flake
and one could get good accuracy in the flake size and that along
with the fact that one just ground it up, put it in a dryer, spit it
out and run it to the press. It had substantially lower manpower
costs. One disadvantage was it took an awful lot of glue to manufacture OSB. One had to get the glue on both sides of the
flakes, and once compared with the amount of glue in a piece of
plywood it was two or three time as much. But if you had the
wood cheap enough, the labor cheap, then you had a fairly good
panel that was a substitute for plywood in most applications.
Eventually through the years the production of OSB in the United States surpassed the production of softwood plywood.
Though today you can go down the street and look at a building
development and you'll notice it uses a lot of OSB, but on the

corners it's a piece of plywood because they want the strength in the main parts of the buildings to add to the practical aspects of the structure. In addition to producing it as a commodity to compete with plywood sheathing, Merlo and L-P also planned to manufacture OSB siding.

But after purchasing the presses from Washington Iron Works, Louisiana-Pacific opted to buy five presses from a Swedish press company. These were 8x14 in platen size and 10 or 12 opening, fairly small by today's standards. It turned out they were made very inexpensively and they were failing structurally and breaking up. After I bought Washington Iron Works, I met with Jim Eisses, Dan Dilworth and Tony Cavadais in Hayward. They wanted to buy a press which turned out they wanted to buy five presses, and I sat there and listened to Jim pound on me for quite a long time. I didn't know him but I got to know him pretty quick. It's like talking to an Australian as the joke goes. You can tell an Australian a mile away but up close you can't tell him much. That's the way with Jim Eisses. You can talk and talk with him until you're blue in the face, but you don't seem to be able to make any points with him. Anyway, Jim excused himself and went to bed, and it was sort of late in the evening, and Dilworth and Cavadais sat there with me and we had another beer and they said one thing you have to do is get this press order. I said I'm glad to hear you're with me. They said look at the press out here at Hayward and the one up in Maine, they're running every day. Those five we put in made in Sweden, those things are falling apart. I said I haven't been to those plants, but I was glad to hear that, and they said they were tired of repairing those damn things so you have to get the order. I said well you guys help me and we'll get it. A couple of weeks later we got the order for five OSB plants and that really helped the Washington Iron Works business. We built the first couple of presses at the plant in Seattle before we had to move. In the meantime I was building the new press plant in Painesville, as that would cut down on our shipping costs from Pennsylvania. We had many economies falling our way in building a plant in Ohio. Those were the rust belt days and I was able to buy very good machine shop tools; there was a lot of it around and no buyers. I equipped a new press plant and we spent about $10 million building that plant and it worked out beautifully. It was 100 feet wide by 400 feet long and it could pick up about 150,000 pounds of weight with a bridge crane. I think we completed the press plant in 1986. We not only got that order from L-P but we got a second order for five presses from them as well.

L-P went on to build nearly two dozen OSB plants and became the number one producer of OSB in the world and still is today. They were trying to become a commodity producer and low cost producer and high volume of sales, and when you're a low cost producer you put as little into the product as you can and sell it for as much as you can. And I think that was their objective, to make it low cost and if they could buy those weed trees at low costs and the next big cost item was glue so you better work on the glue cost and when they worked on the glue costs that's when they got themselves in some trouble. There was a major lawsuit and L-P lost some credibility for a while, and the plywood people tried to take advantage of it, but then you had Georgia-Pacific and Weyerhaeuser and others continuing to build OSB plants which stabilized the reputation of OSB. Merlo, Eisses and Ronnie Paul had a good run for a long while, but they were forced out in the mid 1990s. One of their Colorado plants was accused of trying to fool the board certification authorities and there was also an accusation over tampering with emissions controls, and the lawsuits over defects in its OSB exterior siding. There wasn't much of a chance Merlo and those guys could survive all of that hitting them at once, and they didn't. L-P has been through a couple of presidents since then, and have sold a lot of assets, but the OSB plants mostly remain.

While on the subject of Washington Iron Works, I should address continuous presses. Most of our major press competitors, like Siempelkamp and Dieffenbacher, came out with continuous presses for composite boards like MDF and particleboard, and later on to a lesser degree for OSB that was produced mostly outside of North America, though a couple of OSB plants in the U.S. use the continuous press. We never made the leap. I felt to develop a continuous press was so terribly expensive and ten years in the process of developing it, that I decided I wasn't going to live long enough to try and get one developed. Our figures indicated the cost of making one and maintaining it was going to be so great that we stuck with the multiple-opening presses that WIW had originally designed. We stuck by that and we were successful in doing so. Siempelkamp and Dieffenbacher got into continuous presses and of course they even today fight each other tooth and nail over a job, which means they're selling them at very low costs and there's little money being made in them. As long as we had the expertise and could manufacture inexpensively, we could outsell them in almost all the cases.

Until I sold Coe in 2000, we never did slow down in our pace of acquisitions. To hit the highlights, following the purchase of Washington Iron Works in 1984, that same year we bought Ward Systems, which manufactured moisture detectors for applications in lumber and panels. In 1985 we bought Albany International, a longtime manufacturer of sawmill machinery, and Saab Systems, which produced scanning and optimization systems for edgers, trimmers and gang saws in a sawmill. This technology was combined with what we already had evolved into our D-tec scanning and optimization system, which we pushed into lumber defect detection and grading applications. In 1989 we bought Mann-Russell Electronics, which was a pioneer in radio frequency machinery for engineered wood products. In 1992 we bought another longtime sawmill equipment company, Prescott Iron Works. In 1997, we purchased Pathex Ltd., a manufacturer of presses for composition board as well as rubber materials.

In the 1980s we probably spent the bulk of our engineering and research dollars on developing new high speed sawmill equipment. It took an inordinate amount of time on our part, but we felt the opportunity was there to make substantial strides in obtaining higher levels of recovery. The innovations and devices of machines come only as a result of their making something happen for someone else. Improved recovery is the name of our game. Between our high speed small log sawmills, in trying to improve recovery in three dimensional scan from the old two plane scanning, and the work we did in grade scanning, we took some big steps.

In addition to basic lumber manufacturing, we saw a great deal of development coming with engineered lumber and saw many of our customers getting into that, whether it was fingerjointing or edge gluing or glulam beams. Our purchase of Mann-Russell fit into that. I always enjoyed trying to take the technology one or two steps beyond the level where it was before. But if I hadn't enjoyed that, I shouldn't have been in this business. It's the only thing we have to live for. We stand still and we aren't advancing our technology then someone is going to catch up with us tomorrow and suddenly we're losing ground. We always had the basic philosophy that we're only going to succeed no better than our ability to innovate and develop new ideas, and oftentimes that began with the purchase of another company.

In addition to specific machinery, these companies we acquired brought more repair parts and service to Coe. That's really the most profitable end of your business in the first place. Each of these companies had large bases of equipment out in the field, so it was a source of repair part sales and as a result we were able to justify pretty easily the purchase of these companies. We brought most of these people together in Portland. We always found a way of hiring people who had the ideas. We had a reputation of being fair with people. Each one of those acquisitions brought in different ways and means of doing business, different attitudes, and trying to keep those ideas and people pointed in one direction as our company was a very time consuming effort.

By the time I was done, we had expanded four times at Tigard in addition to buying the Georgia-Pacific plant next door. We in effect doubled our plant facilities there and in the meantime we had built two big buildings in Painesville,

I would say our biggest expansion came in lumber equipment as it accounted for thirty precent of our sales volume. One business we never got into, which was related to forest products, was the pulp and paper industry. We looked at drying pulp at one time and it was just so far fetched from what we were doing. We didn't do much more than spend four to six months of engineering time in figuring out how we could do it and be competitive. We had to either be competitive or we were just waving our hands in the wind and wasting our time. When it looked like it was going to be the latter, we ended the effort. In a development project somewhere someone has to make a decision as to whether you have an opportunity for success or whether you're going down the road of failure. It always fell on my shoulders, which is why up until I sold the company I was still very active. To make a logical decision, I had to be very close to the development process to understand what was going on so that I could make the decision as to whether to spend more money or just junk it and forget about it. We were always in the process of trying to make those decisions. The pulp and paper decision was a relatively quick and easy one.

CHAPTER NINETEEN

THE WORLD OF PATENTS

Just when you think you've encountered all of the problems that might come your way in operating a business, you're hit with another surprise. Have you ever heard of The Patent King? I am talking about Jerome Lemelson. He was only a step away from wreaking havoc on our industry in the 1990s, including Coe and me. Lemelson began his "patents career" in the 1950s, with many of his patents for simple toys, like a beanie with a propeller on top. But the toy companies weren't inclined to license his patents and Lemelson sued them for stealing his ideas. He began seeking patents for all kinds of devices and technologies. They were taken to the patent office and reviewed and everything was accomplished excepting he did not let them issue. In other words they did not become a viable patent whereby he could protect his interest. He held them back and didn't let them issue until the late 1980s and early 1990s. The thing was, a patent application could be delayed through a "continuation."

Applicants could modify or add claims to their so-called inventions, even amend them with real products that had come on the market, which they could claim to have invented because they had applied for the patents many years before. Lemelson became an expert in using these continuations to keep his patents from becoming a real patent, or issuing as it was called.

Many of Lemelson's patents were related to machine vision, which he further amended to include bar-coding. He finally allowed these patents to issue and he started raising patent issues and seeking license fees not against the new manufacturers of these technologies but from the users of these products, which as *Fortune* magazine wrote in a story about this, included just about every company on the planet. First he sent letters to all the off-shore automobile companies in Europe and Japan and eventually filed a lawsuit, and those various companies ended up settling with him for a half billion dollars. Then he went after the U.S. auto industry and received large settlements from Ford, GM and Chrysler. He of course started with the biggest manufacturers in the world in the automobile industry, but he went after all sorts of companies, railroad companies, chemical companies and he was so successful it was almost vulgar, collecting a billion and a half dollars and probably more than that in licensing fees.

When Coe started getting into advanced technology such as computer and scanners, prior to say 1975, there wasn't any of that type apparatus used in the industry. We acquired some laser scanning devices and various other software that we used to operate it. As we went along we filed patent applications for the technology and the software that we were using and we had a substantial number of patents that were issued. When we sold equipment that included software in machinery that our patents were related to, we stated in the proposal for sale that we would hold the user harmless in case of patent infringements. Well in the mid 1990s Lemelson and his team finally got to the point of going after the wood products manufacturers such as Weyerhaeuser, Georgia-Pacific, Willamette and others. He got a list of those companies and told them this machine vision type equipment that was bought from Coe infringed on his patents number so and so and we expect you to pay us a percentage of the purchase price as a royalty. Anyway these manufacturers like Weyerhaeuser and Georgia-Pacific came to us and said wait a minute, you sold us this equipment and you said you had patents to cover it, it's your responsibility to hold us harmless. You can imagine the anxiety this development caused me, considering the success this Lemelson fella had been having. A meeting was called of mostly engineering people from Weyerhaeuser, Georgia-Pacific and Willamette and we met at our office in Portland. We all decided that the industry as such would put a similar letter together and send it back to him and say we bought this equipment from Coe and Coe has patents for their equipment and we don't believe your patents are effective in this case and unless you can prove conclusively that the Coe equipment infringes, then we're not going to recognize your claim for royalties.

It was at that time two or three companies from other industries had challenged Lemelson and told him they weren't going to pay him royalties and they got a court judgement that indicated his patents weren't any good, they were invalid. The patents had been applied for in 1957 and he didn't allow them to be issued until 1992 and patents have only a twenty year life under the new rules anyway. Meanwhile the letters were written by these various plywood producers who in as much told him to go to heck and we waited and waited and never heard anything more from him. We think it was because this judgment was handed down in this entirely different industry that indicated his patents weren't any good, and also Lemelson himself had gotten liver cancer and died of it in the latter part of 1997. There again, in talking about patents, and whether to go through the trials of obtaining them, had we not had some patents we might have had some responsibility for these people that had bought our equipment. Just another day at the office.

The Coe business was really accelerating in the mid 1990s, which meant we were all moving fast all of the time. Who knows if that contributed to the triple bypass surgery I underwent in 1997? Or maybe it was the anxiety caused by the patents saga I just spoke about. Or perhaps it was the fact that I had begun the process of trying to sell the company, which I'll address in a moment. It was probably none of these, but one night I felt some pain in my chest while sleeping and I thought it was because I was sleeping on my arm. That went on for a couple of weeks. Then one morning I was sitting at my desk at about nine o'clock and I felt this same pain and I thought holy smoke I've got to find out what in the world this is. It was an aching pain that would come and go. If I got up and moved around it would seem to relieve itself, and then it would reoccur when I settled down and wasn't performing any movement. So I got in the car and drove over to nearby Meridian Park Hospital. I parked in the emergency parking lot and went in and told them I felt badly. They gave me some blood tests, examined me a little bit and said you have a blockage and you're going to have to have open heart surgery or a stint. The doctor said he thought I was too old to have the stint and we're going to take you in and give you an angiogram. The first thing I know I was in the emergency operating room having an angiogram and they found where the blockage was in the lower section of my heart. I could see where it was. I was semi sedated but I could see it on the television screen and they could point out the blockage and they said we think you should have surgery. And I said what about a stint, I've heard about those. The doctor said I'm going to meet with the staff this afternoon and we'll consider that. They came in about six o'clock and said we've decided if you're willing we'll try a stint but we're not sure how effective it will be. I said I think I would rather have that than open heart surgery. They took me to the operating room the next day and I had the stint put in.

They pronounced the operation as successful. I stayed overnight and they released me and I felt okay. That lasted for about a year and I began to feel that same pain again. I went back and he said that stint is not going to do the job and you're going to have to have open heart surgery. I said okay I'm not going to argue anymore about it. I went to the operating room and had three way bypass. They took a vein out of my left leg to use for the procedure. It was successful. After a few days in the hospital they told me I could leave and do whatever I wanted to do. Two days later I was on a plane to Houston for a meeting and right after that I went to Painesville. I still had stitches in my chest area, but I didn't have any pain. It's been good ever since.

The Coe logo may have changed through the years, but the basic operating principles, the commitment to quality, and devotion to the customer never faltered.

Precision engineering and manufacturing was part of the Coe formula, from its earliest years at the Painesville plant, to the modern era, as shown in the same plant, opposite page.

APRIL 30, 1909.

The Telegraph-Republican subscribers will facilitate good service by promptly reporting late, irregular or missed papers. Both phones, 42.

THE TELEGRAPH-REPUBLICAN

WEATHER.

Showers and colder tonight; Saturday, partly cloudy and colder, probably rain or snow.

Vol. 18, No. 102.   PAINESVILLE, OHIO, FRIDAY, APRIL 30, 1909.   ONE CENT.

TERRIFIC THUNDER STORM WITH WIND ACCOMPANIMENT HITS CITY

Steeple of Fairport Church Falls and Painesville House Is Struck by Lightning—Rainfall Was Unusually Heavy.

A storm that began early Thursday evening and raged intermittently throughout the night did more or less damage to Painesville and vicinity. The lightning and thunder accompaniment was of unusual severity and the rainfall the greatest in recent years. The rainfall measured 1.87 inches, which is twice as much rain as has fallen since January 1. Many trees were damaged by the wind that came with the storm and onion fields in Painesville, Perry and Madison were flooded.

House Struck by Bolt.

The residence of Arthur Patton on Richmond street was struck by a bolt during the night and the shingling torn off one side. The damage was only slight.

Church Steeple Topples.

A steeple on the Lutheran church in Fairport was blown over but no other damage was done at the Harbor.

Telephone Damage.

The local telephone companies had their troubles. Many phones were put out of commission and a few poles were blown down.

River Very High.

The river was up to its limit and in many places overflowing the banks. The water is said to be higher than at any time during the past year.

Washout on the C. P. & A.

The storm did more or less damage along the C. P. & A. and at Mahl's crossing near Geneva, the rain washed out near a culvert and the track sunk. It was impossible to run over the damaged piece of track and passengers were compelled to transfer.

FUNERAL SERVICES FOR A LITTLE BOY

MANY ATTEND LAST SAD RITES FOR SON OF FRANK SCHAFFER.

The funeral services for little Glenn Schaffer, aged nineteen months and two days, was held at the home of his parents, Mr. and Mrs. Frank Schaffer, on Jackson street, Thursday, April 29. Rev. T. F. Phillips of the M. E. church conducted the services. Music was furnished by Mrs. S. B. Park and Mrs. George Sherman.

"TRUE FRIENDSHIP" WILL BE HIS SUBJECT

REV. A. A. KIEHLE WILL GIVE IN-

MAN MISSING SINCE LAST NOVEMBER FISHED OUT OF RIVER BY L. S. CREW

Proves to be Jerome Murdock, Sailor on the Steamer Marsalia—Relatives Have Been Searching For Missing Man.

After six months of hoping against hope the relatives will now know the fate of Jerome Murdock, missing since the middle of last November. Murdock's decomposed body was fished from the river by the life saving crew Friday morning as it was being swept past the station by the swift current.

A shipping paper issued from ____ lodo identified the remains. Letters were also found ____ discolored and ____ ed. A dollar ____ was in one of ____ marks of iden ____ by Coroner H. ____ called to the ____ R. D. Keener ____ then removed ____ Coroner Ams ____ was some tal ____ time Murdock ____ was so badly ____ would be dif ____

marks of violence if they should have existed.

At the time Murdock was missing he was a sailor on the steamer Marsalia which was in the upper slip in Fairport. Members of the crew told August Wulff of the incident at the time. Mr. Wulff stated Friday that he did not know of the suspicion that Murdock was a victim of foul play. He said he knew all the members of the crew but heard nothing

CHIEF P____ WOMA____

Two plain ____ and costs and ____ ian Friday ____

SHIPMENT VALUED AT $40,000 IS BEING LOADED BY THE COE COMPANY

Local Manufacturing Concern Fills Its Largest Order. Twelve Carloads of Machinery Going to Vladivostok May 15.

The future of the Coe Manufacturing Co. looks particularly bright just at present. In addition to many domestic orders this company is now loading the largest foreign order in its history. Twelve carloads valued at $40,000 will leave here for New York City Monday and will be delivered aboard boat to sail May 15 for Vladivostok, Siberia, the city made famous during the Japanese-Russian war. The shipment is consigned to the Skidelski company, Russian manufacturers of veneers.

In the shipment there is a full line of veneer machinery which includes two rotary machines, clippers, veneer saws, wringers, grinder, cold roller dry kiln, glue room machinery, presses, tapping machines, jointers, veneer scrapers and other minor parts that go to make up a modern veneer plant.

The country where this big shipment is headed for is very rich in timber and surpasses in this respect any country or section of country on the globe.

The order was secured several months ago when representatives of the Russian company visited this city.

SHIPMENT VALUED AT $40,000 IS BEING LOADED BY THE COE COMPANY

Local Manufacturing Concern Fills Its Largest Order. Twelve Carloads of Machinery Going to Vladivostok May 15.

The future of the Coe Manufacturing Co. looks particularly bright just at present. In addition to many domestic orders this company is now loading the largest foreign order in its history. Twelve carloads valued at $40,000 will leave here for New York City Monday and will be delivered aboard boat to sail May 15 for Vladivostok, Siberia, the city made famous during the Japanese-Russian war. The shipment is consigned to the Skidelski company, Russian manufacturers of veneers.

In the shipment there is a full line of veneer machinery which includes two rotary machines, clippers, veneer saws, wringers, grinder, cold roller dry kiln, glue room machinery, presses, tapping machines, jointers, veneer scrapers and other minor parts that go to make up a modern veneer plant.

The country where this big shipment is headed for is very rich in timber and surpasses in this respect any country or section of country on the globe.

The order was secured several months ago when representatives of the Russian company visited this city.

Coe Manufacturing ran into some hard times during the World War I decade, but one of the bright moments was a huge shipment of veneer machinery to a Russian producer in Siberia.

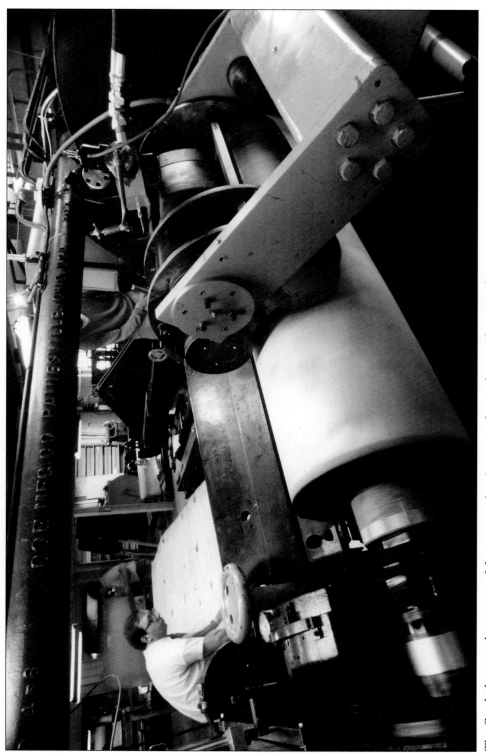

The Coe lathe was always one of the company's primary products, along with veneer dryers.

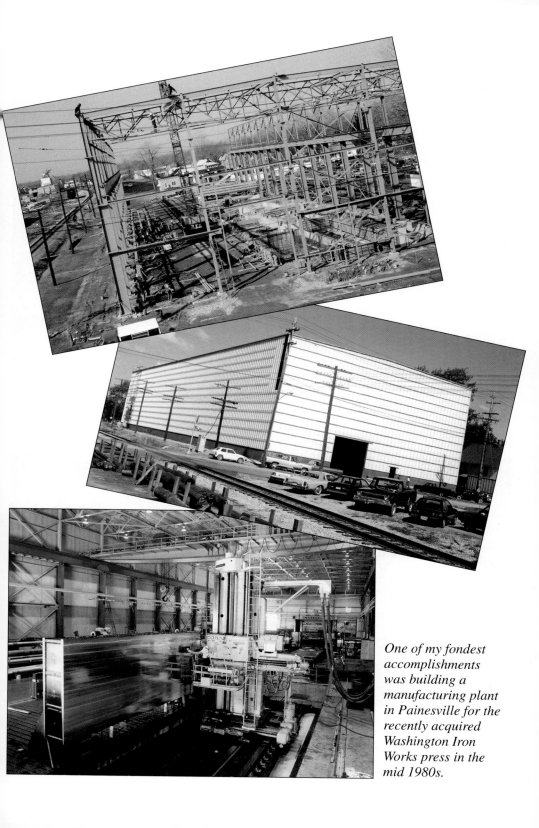

One of my fondest accomplishments was building a manufacturing plant in Painesville for the recently acquired Washington Iron Works press in the mid 1980s.

Left to right, Gene Knokey, Ralph Gage, Don Howell and Rolf Steberg.

Left to right, Mike Coleman, Irv McMahan, Frank Milbourn III and yours truly.

My wife, Sue, and I share a moment at the dedication of the Fred W. Fields Center for the Visual Arts at Lewis & Clark College.

Faithful companion, Kate.

I had the privilege of delivering the commencement address at Lake Erie College in Painesville, Ohio, and received an honorary degree.

Kenneth Ford's birthday party was a festive affair. Seated, left to right, Dale Fischer, Fischer-Marcola Lumber; Bob Vadnais, Totem Equipment; Kenneth Ford, Roseburg Forest Products; yours truly; Eric Hoffman, Hoffman Construction. Standing, left to right, Willie La Grande, La Grande Supply Company; Gene Knokey, Coe Manufacturing; Dick Cole, Aion Insurance; Bill Swindells, Willamette Industries; Frank Spears, attorney; Marshall Leeper, U.S. Plywood; Bill Nicholson, Nicholson Manufacturing; Allyn Ford, Roseburg Forest Products; John Stevens, Roseburg Forest Products; Harry Demorest, Columbia Plywood.

Kenneth Ford and I remained close until he passed away in 1997.

CHAPTER TWENTY

SO LONG OLD FRIEND

A round 1995 I decided it was time for me to start thinking about what I could do with the company. I was 72 years old and I decided all of a sudden I wasn't going to live forever. There was the thought of turning it over to the employees. But I hadn't prepared sufficiently to do that. There were people like Gene Knokey and Art McGee, they weren't quite as old as myself but they were approaching 65 years old and thinking of retirement. So the key guys were looking to retire and that meant that I hadn't really done my job properly in bringing on younger people who could take on and run the business. I could have formed an ESOP, but I always had the feeling that if somebody went broke trying to buy the business I wouldn't want to be a party to someone else's failure. I'd hate to leave innocent people stranded, including suppliers and customers.

The Milbourn boys had worked for me for a number of years but they had left and found other things to do and they didn't want it back. I decided I should be looking around and trying to find someone with sufficient means to carry on the business and also to pay me what I thought the company was worth. The company's revenue had continued to grow rather exponentially since I had purchased it. Part of it was due to the more expensive modern technologies we had helped to develop, such as the X-Y lathe charger, and a big part of it was our purchase of numerous companies and product lines, such as the Washington Iron Works presses, that we continued to develop and market and which substantially enhanced our sales volume. When I first started thinking about selling the company, its best revenue years were still ahead of it. About $95 million was the most revenue we got, and that was in 1998.

I informally engaged a fella named Jimmy Miller to assist me with ths process. He was a guy who helped Georgia-Pacific acquire various companies and had helped Willamette Industries. He was the president of an investment company located in New York and was very well respected in the timber business. He grew up in Seaside on the Oregon coast and had grown up around the timber industry and worked his way up through the company from a ribbon clerk if you will to the presidency and he was a smart guy. There were plenty of people that were interested in buying a good company that was profitable or had been profitable for a number of years. So there was no problem in finding someone who was interested. The problem was finding someone who was interested that had the appropriate financial wherewithal and had the experience to run a business such as this. We went to ten or twelve different companies and they either had one or the other; they either had the money and no capability, or they had the capability and no money. In the case of them not having the financial wherewithal they expected me to do the financing, which I couldn't get real excited about.

We came close to making a proposition to Fibreboard. But Fibreboard back in the 60s and 70s was in the business of making various types of fiber products, paper, soft board, and in that they used flaked asbestos and over the years they had a long history of having to go to court over these asbestos claims. Over a ten year period or so they put cash in reserve for having to pay asbestos claims. They hired a new president who was a very sharp individual and he got to digging around and found they had insurance that covered them on things such as asbestos, or matters similar to asbestos. As a result they were able to prove this with Lloyds of London, which meant all of the money they had pigeonholed away as a reserve to pay the claims all became loose and free. Fibreboard was near Sacramento, California and that was an area that was quite short on timber. Being a timber based company they had to start looking for another area of business to enter and a business that was profitable and they had the cash to do that. Jimmy Miller was on their board of directors, so he pointed them in my direction and we worked at this thing for several months and it looked like a natural fit. They were in the plywood business, in the fiberboard business and they knew the machinery that we sold and manufactured and as a result it seemed to be something that they had knowledge of and were anxious to buy. About the time we were getting ready to close, one of the Georgia-Pacific plants in Fort Dodge, Iowa found that Coe had rebuilt one of the old dryers and used asbestos in the installation. It was around 1970 that all this raucous about asbestos started, so this dryer had been built and installed before that time. Fibreboard's attorney told them you just got out of an asbestos situation, you sure as heck don't want to get back into another one. That destroyed the whole deal. Two or three months later we got a summary judgment that said Coe was one of ten or fifteen people that might have been involved but it was proven we had no responsibility for that particular problem. But the Fibreboard negotiation was over.

Jimmy Miller and I kept on investigating various companies. He had contacts in New York and I talked to many other companies. Again, they either had the money and no expertise, or they had no money and a lot of expertise. Some of the ones who had the finances, they got it by various means and they would cut corners and maybe they had a reputation like some of these venture capitalists that we know of today. I turned several people down who wanted to buy it on nothing down and take forever to pay or pay if you catch me.

Then, a certain venture capitalist firm came along and they had plenty of financing and they were operating several machine tool companies and various machine type manufacturing businesses, mostly related to the steel business. I had found out about them through an old acquaintance from our industry who had retired but who was working with a company in Chicago, and he turned us over to this acquisition company in Chicago who in turn turned it over to the company I eventually sold to. They were manufacturers, they had engineering people and technical people and MIT graduates. It just seemed that these fellas had the wherewithal to do a good job. I thought, well, if we can work out a deal, we'll do it with these people because they do have the expertise and the financing. That's the way it came about and so after five years I thought I had found someone that I thought was capable of doing the job, even though they turned out to be a bunch of flakes.

They did their due diligence over eight months, but I confined them to talking to myself or to my financial vice president or my accountant or attorney as I didn't want to advertise that I was trying to sell the company and find that our employees were dropping out and going to work for a competitor. Many times these things fall apart and don't develop into a meaningful relationship so I had to confine their due diligence to working our books and looking at the information we had. At no time did they ever reject the selling price. That wasn't a question. The questions they asked were how much business do you have, how much profit, how do you arrive at the profit levels you are expecting, all of which were good questions. They were able to look at our list of backlog of orders and our list of customers that we had provided equipment to, people like Georgia-Pacific, Weyerhaeuser, Boise and Willamette; everyone in the business so they couldn't complain about that. We had a backlog of business. At the end of May in the year I sold in 2000, we had a backlog of $87 million, $82 million of which was to be delivered by the first of November of 2000. There was $5 million worth of orders that was to be delivered after year end of 2000. At the same time we would have generated additional business that could be delivered in 2000, certainly spare parts and so forth, so during those six months from May through October we would certainly have generated more than $5 million worth of business. We were looking at more than $85 million of business in the year 2000. When I bought the company in 1976, they had done about $12 million in sales. In those days they would generate maybe a hundred thousand dollars worth of sales per employee per year. After I bought it, starting along in the 70s and 80s we got into more sophisticated equipment with the computer controls and laser scanners, and when we did that the value of the equipment goes up and we were getting about $120,000 per man per year. In 1999, my last full year, we had about 750 employees and we did a little over $90 million in sales.

Like I said, none of the companies that we had discussed this with ever questioned my selling price; now there were people who made offers that were just fishing expeditions and I didn't consider them legitimate buyers. I might have sold at a lower price but I didn't have a reason to lower the price, no one was questioning it. So a deal was struck in April 2000. I had property in Canada, twelve acres up there and a couple hundred thousand square feet of buildings that Coe Company leased from me that I had bought because it was an old foundry site and there was contamination and I didn't want the company to be saddled with contaminated property. So I had bought the property and leased it to the company. I kept that when I sold the company. We had securities and various other things that there was no point in selling. I was running an S corporation. The earnings went straight to me without paying corporate taxes. I just switched the cash and securities over to myself. We also had liabilities I had to satisfy. In the end I sold Coe for a satisfactory amount.

It turned out that this venture firm was somewhat questionable. When it came to making the purchase, I think they wanted a pound of flesh you might say. They said we can only pay you about eighty percent in cash. I thought well that's pretty good. If I don't get any more, I've still gotten the monkey off my back so to speak. They owed me $10 million in deferred payments to be paid over a three year period and in equal quarterly payments to be paid over that three years. And they owed me $5 million in consulting fees. I was supposed to stay on for three years as a consultant. So they owed me $15 million and I don't know whether I should say this, but within three weeks after I sold them the company, their chairman came in and said we have a new president in place. He seems to be concerned about your presence here so I've got to ask you to leave. Why don't you just move out at your convenience and we'll pay you the consulting fee and if we need help from you we'll call you but unless we do call you there's no point in you being involved. I was really disappointed with that because I felt they needed some experienced people to run the business. I was concerned about how you announce it to the employees and to the customers, how you assimilate getting along with the new people, and how you resolve accounts receivable.

They proceeded to discharge probably forty or fifty percent of the keys guys in the company very shortly after they fired me. I can't say we had the best people in the world but they were the best people in that position that were available for our business. They thought they could find people out of MIT and various other engineering schools that were smarter than that dumb guy who owned the business. They did it their way. They moved in a whole group of so called experienced people and proceeded to take Coe Company down the drain. It didn't make any sense at all. They were supposed to give me a financial statement as they moved along. I couldn't get a financial statement for two years, and the first one I got indicated they had lost $55 million the first year they had the company. And I know they should have made $15 million. We lost money one year when I had the company. I had left the company with almost $20 million in cash in it; they apparently took that out of the company right away and spent that somewhere else I guess. Then they began selling off anything that was loose on one end. They sold a lot of equipment, they sold the properties and buildings in Portland, they didn't do that just immediately but they made it known it was for sale and they eventually found buyers for it. Along November of that same year, 2000, they wrote me a letter and mind you they had not been making their payments to me and they said we believe that you defrauded us and we're not going to pay you anymore. That hit me pretty strong. We wrote them a letter and said if you want to do that we're probably going to take some legal action. They said let's have a meeting and we'll discuss the things we think you defrauded us on. We kept waiting for them to call to arrange a meeting and they never did call. And we never had a meeting. We gave them another letter and said if we don't hear from you we're going to take some action. Shortly thereafter we filed suit in federal court in Portland.

We had an arbitration clause, and the court appointed a judge or magistrate as it was to handle the case. We met in Portland with the key people of their company. As it turned out, nothing happened. They offered to give me a million dollars to settle everything. I said I wasn't interested. We went on for a year and every time something was suggested they would delay it and delay and delay and that went on for a couple of years. Then we went back to the court and said what can we do. They said we have another magistrate that we think is a real master in matters of arbitration. So we met with the judge. He listened to the story for about an hour and said gentlemen I've got better things to do than this. He pointed to me and said, if you lose you're going to appeal it. He pointed to them, if you lose you're going to appeal. We're not going to settle anything here so I'm excusing myself and that was the end of that. We went on for another six months and the federal court handed it over to a female judge in Eugene. She had the reputation for having settled almost every case that was brought to her. She said I've got a magistrate and he is an outstanding person in arbitrating matters of this kind. So we met in Eugene and sat there for two days and argued back and forth and the final result was that they offered two million dollars. I said no. The judge said okay we're going to go to court. By the time everybody got all the details together, that took another year.

We went to court here in Portland with the judge from Eugene. She had an office in the courthouse in Portland. We had a jury trial. It went on for six days and finally got to the point where the judge hammered the gavel in the middle of the afternoon on the sixth day and said this thing shouldn't be in court. Obviously there's a wrongdoing here, she said, and the jury knows it, I know it, we all know it. I'm going to try and settle this thing. I'm not going to release the jury, I'm going to put you on hold and you can wait in the lounge. If we can settle this thing then you'll be released, but if not we'll be back in here with the trial. We went back into the judge's chambers and she put the other company's people in her conference room. She went back and forth between us to try and get this thing resolved. I don't know what she said to them, but she must have said something like you guys you have to admit that you owe Mr. Fields money and you better be prepared to pay him or if we go back in that court room you're going to be damn sorry you did.

She came out and said Mr. Fields what do you want, what will you settle for? I looked at my one male attorney and asked him what suggestions he had; he said I wouldn't touch that one with a ten foot pole. That's your decision. I had a lady attorney; I said Susan what would you suggest? She said I wouldn't touch it either. I looked at the judge who was sitting two feet across from me at the desk. I told her they owed me $15 million, that I had spent an awful lot of money on attorneys and I was also entitled to interest. The way I figured it, the $15 million they owed me was to be offset by some product liability problems that the company had, and we had six or seven million dollars in accounts receivable that may not have been collectable, and so probably six or seven million would have come off that $15 million. I explained to the judge I had almost $5 million in attorney's fees.

And then there was the matter of interest on the $15 million, but if you took the $7 million off the $15 million that's the interest on $8 million, so I said I will settle for $15 million. She says is that it? I said that's it.

She went back into the office with the opposition and said Mr. Fields wants $15 million. She was in there for almost an hour and I guess she repeated that if we have to go back in the court room you're going to be damn sorry. She finally came out and said okay they finally agreed they're going to pay you $15 million, and she said she had asked if they had the money and they assured her they had the money and will pay the money within 30 days. She said she told them if they didn't have the money they were really going to hear about it. Then she said they have one more request. I said what's that? She said they want you to sign a confidentiality agreement that you won't talk about the settlement. I said no. The reason I said no was because we knew of two companies they had bought that they had done the same thing with them and driven them to arbitration and settling out of court. We knew that each of these companies had signed these confidentiality agreements because we had called them and they wouldn't talk to us. They wouldn't tell us what happened so we were on our own. The judge said Mr. Fields you're getting everything you wanted. I said your honor they hurt too many people, they hurt me, they hurt an awful lot of our employees by laying them off. Now three or four years has gone by and they've just riddled the company in the eyes of the customers, they've done a terrible job of supplying service and machinery to all of these customers that we've supplied over the years and I don't want to see any more of it. And if it happens again, and somebody wants to ask me about it, I'm going to tell them what happened to me. She said I don't know, I'll go back and try. So she went back into the conference room with them and about ten minutes later she came back out and this time she had both thumbs in the air with her fists clenched and she was skipping. She said Mr. Fields, "You've got it, you've got it!" I think she was as happy as I was.

I got everything I was entitled. The only thing I couldn't reconstruct was the damage done to the company and my employees. It was really a long and distasteful process that was finally settled in 2005. I always had confidence that we were on the right side of the law and we weren't being unfair to them, they were being unfair to me. Miller Nash in Portland was my attorney. They had done a lot of work for Georgia-Pacific, Willamette and various timber companies.

Absolutely I wish I had sold to somebody else. Absolutely, I wish I had. But I had looked for five years to find somebody who had the finances and experience to run a machinery business. A machinery business is not all that complicated, but if you don't have any experience, experience is awfully important, and they seemed to have it. Not having a long-term development plan of getting in-house management to take over and run the company turned out to be a major regret for me. I thought I could find a company outside of our people that had resources and the wherewithal to make Coe a better company. I thought there was a lot of opportunity in the export business, even establish a plant in China or Russia or Germany.

Another disappointment for me, and perhaps this was inevitable no matter when I sold the company, was that we had always had a fairly healthy list of research and development projects, some of which came about through our own people and some were ideas of customers. We oftentimes worked with customers like Weyerhaeuser and Georgia-Pacific that wanted to develop certain pieces of equipment. At one time a fella with Weyerhaeuser said we've done more successful developments with Coe Company than we've done with our own research and development department. He was expressing a keen appreciation for the work we had done. My point is that when I sold the company we had numerous projects in research and development; four or five of them were nearing maturity, to the point where we had made a model or prototype and put it in and operated it and it was nearly successful and we were about ready to go out and sell it. Many others were ideas and sketches and thoughts that needed a great deal of energy and engineering. I was disappointed in that we didn't get more of those done. You only do those as time and money becomes available.

As for some of our Coe long-timers. Gene Knokey had retired before this came about. Art McGee had just retired. There were three or four other key engineers who were still with the company whom they let go, people with the Washington Iron Works engineering group and Coe's engineering group. Ralph Gage stayed on. They needed him in the South. In the West they had Alan Knokey, Gene's son, who had worked for me. Before I left they asked me who I thought should run the Coe business in Portland and I said Alan Knokey. They proceeded to give him the job and six months later took him out of that position and he drifted backwards several times until he was relegated to an individual sales representative. Then they closed the Portland office. In early 2009, After USNR took over the bankrupt operation, Alan called me and said he had been promoted to general manager of manufacturing, engineering and sales, and I said, Jesus, that's where I left you. I guess USNR recognized he had some ability. Now Alan manages the old Coe business in Painesville and Coe appears to be making somewhat of a comeback. I know they've sold plywood machinery in Russia. The irony of it all.

At one point I looked at buying back Coe. It became very entangled. In 2002 the new Coe owner—the one that bought the company from me—bought Newnes McGehee in Canada from CAE and formed Coe Newnes McGehee or CNM in Salmon Arm, British Columbia. This was basically the sawmill part of the old Coe business combined with two other established sawmill companies. The new owner sold the buildings and properties in Oregon, but weren't able to sell all the properties in Painesville. Eventually they had to declare bankruptcy in Canada, and that part of the business was purchased by USNR in the summer of 2008. The same thing more or less happened to the Coe business in Painesville, mostly the old panel machinery business. I heard that the USNR people paid a dollar for it. It really broke my heart to see my old company go the way it went.

When they took the company in Canada bankrupt I had gone up to the Salmon Arm office and thought I would try to buy Coe back. It so happened I was there the day the bankruptcy proceedings were held in Vancouver BC and when I walked in the door there was a representative of KPMG, the accounting firm there, and he said Mr. Fields, I know you're interested in what's going on, and he told me the bankruptcy judge was selling the business and it looked like USNR was going to buy it and as a result of that the judge said to USNR if you want to buy Coe of USA we'll sell it to you for a dollar. I had talked to USNR earlier. I didn't realize they were that close to coming to an agreement. I had told the fella at USNR I would buy Coe back. USNR was primarily a sawmill machinery manufacturer and I thought maybe if they bit off the Newnes McGehee part of the business they would be interested in selling Coe. I talked to him afterward and he said I've got so many entanglements that I don't know what we bought and how much we owe and until I get it straightened out I'm not interested in doing anything but getting all the details and facts on the table. That was the last meaningful discussion I had with him and he never came back to me and said I'm ready to sell Coe.

I've never really gotten Coe out of my system. I still worry about it and am concerned about it. When I sold it, the investment group that bought it wasn't very kind to me and made it very difficult for me to keep in touch. Today I try to know generally what's going on in the business. Had I bought Coe in 2008 I would have hired back as many employees as I could. I would have picked someone to run the business and I would have overseen it. What I had intended to do was to see if I could get a loan to pay off their liabilities and put the company back on its feet. As I mentioned, when I sold the business we had these research and development projects at various stages of completion. Since then one or two of those developments have become very good developments and have supported the company with fresh business that they would not have had otherwise. But there were several developments that left the company because they fired the people that did the development work and they went to other companies or started their own businesses. But that's not unusual. It happens every day. I would have bought the business, tried to keep the people, and if it made a profit I would have taken the profit and paid down the bank loan and turned it over to the people who were running it and who could make the business grow and prosper.

The Coe business seems to be making progress today, but the economy has been such you can hardly give machinery away. The previous owner, before USNR, didn't believe in spending money on development. If they had something that was worth a dollar they wanted to sell it and get the dollar. They were trying to recuperate any cash benefit from the sale of any of the assets. They weren't interested in speculating on new developments. In all the time I operated Coe Company we always made a little bit of money and the important thing for the company was that I was never a big spender personally and neither was my wife and we kept reinvesting the money we had in the business. If someone came along who wanted to sell their business and it looked like it could add to our customers' well being, we reinvested in it. Had we been a company with many shareholders we wouldn't have had the money to invest as we likely would have had to pay it out in dividends to the shareholders.

CHAPTER TWENTY-ONE

TEN GOOD MEN

I was hesitant to do this, but at the continued urging from the editor and publisher of this book, I now present ten men who had a profound influence on me and our industry. I've spoken about some of them already elsewhere in this book, but I feel they deserve a little bit of additional recognition here.

FRANK MILBOURN, JR.

I had worked for Frank for thirty years before I bought Coe Company. He was really my mentor. We never had a harsh word between us. After I bought Coe Company he continued to work for me. He came to the office every day until he became ill and passed away. He was so fair and honest with everyone including me. Once I met him, he was a lifelong friend and associate. He couldn't have been a more pleasant individual. When he decided to sell Coe, we never negotiated the purchase price. He had been negotiating with two other companies that had not developed into sales. I decided when I was considering the purchase of the company that I was not going to negotiate or bargain with him about the price. Either I found it to be comfortable for me to buy the company and pay his price or I was not going to buy it at all. When he told me what he wanted, I said I'll buy it. It was an association you couldn't find many places in this world.

His father was a tougher individual, more of a taskmaster, and Frank Jr. grew up under him and had a better and smoother way about him. After his father passed away in 1957, Frank Jr. took over the company from that point until he sold it to me in 1976. In addition to his stellar reputation in our industry, he was admired in the Painesville area and very active locally. He received honors such as the Painesville Chamber of Commerce Man of the Year. Of course he was a Princetonian through and through and stayed active as an alumnus. At his death, he had been married for more than fifty years to Lucy Buehler. He died in the Cleveland Clinic on December 8, 1989, from complications with pneumonia and a severe stroke, at the age of 76. He made my experiences at Coe very pleasant and enjoyable to say nothing of the successes we enjoyed.

KENNETH FORD

Kenneth Ford was a very good customer of ours. When I first met him he was not in the plywood business, but he had just bought the equipment for his plant number one that went in at Dillard, Oregon. At that time I was a field engineer for Coe. I was asked to supervise the installation of the lathe and the dryer and the other auxiliary equipment we had sold. My first meeting with him was the day I arrived on the West Coast. I had gone to Roseburg late in the afternoon and I walked through the skeleton of the plant building to determine where the job stood and what I had to do the next day. On my way walking out of the building lo and behold I met Kenneth Ford. We introduced ourselves. I said I need to go to dinner and this happens to be my birthday, have you got an idea where I might go? He said I belong to the Elk's Club and why don't you go to dinner with me. That was our first meeting and acquaintance and it was a pleasant experience. In those days you couldn't buy a drink across the bar, you had to carry your own bottle. He had a bottle stored in there and we both had a couple of drinks and we enjoyed ourselves.

During the installation of the equipment I had spent a couple of months there, and every day we would visit and talk about how the job was going and he always had some questions to ask and sometimes he was critical of what I was doing but we always got along very well. He continued to build plywood plants and in the process he was always doing something a little different but he was always doing it first class. He would pick my brain for whatever he thought I knew and he would add whatever he had picked from other people's brains and he always came up with a very first class manufacturing facility with the latest techniques and technology and it was pleasant working with him during those days.

We continued to associate and discuss techniques and technology the rest of his life and most of my working days as well. Kenneth and his first wife, Hallie, lived in Roseburg and had one son and one daughter. Allyn, his son, is now the president of the company and is the CEO. He was always involved in the company but in the days I was around he didn't partake in the manufacturing end of the business very much; he was more of the guy in charge of the logging operations. Kenneth built a hardwood plywood finishing plant, Carmen Panel Company, and named it after his daughter, Carmen . He married again to Bonnie Stanley in the early 1980s. One of our last projects together was the design of a small log line at the sawmill in Dillard. He didn't live to see it start up. Kenneth died of cancer in 1997 at age 88 in Roseburg.

JOHN ELORRIGA

John Elorriga was the chairman of the U.S. Bank and was the person who loaned me the money to buy Coe Company. He had been the president of Evans Products at one time and I'd known him for a number of years. He was with the bank before he went to Evans Products and I think he was a loan officer. He grew up in eastern Oregon and came from a sheep herding family and he had worked his way up through the ranks to the chairman of the bank. John was a nice guy and when it came time to buy Coe Company in 1976, somebody said to me do you know where you could borrow the money. I said, I know the chairman of U.S. Bank, I'd like to start with him. My accountant and I made arrangements to meet him and we talked for about twenty minutes and discussed the financial statements of Coe. John knew the name Coe, though we hadn't necessarily done any business with him. He knew the reputation of Coe and had confidence in the company and I assume myself

After considerable discussion, he said, well, just a minute, and he called a vice president to join us and said these fellows want to borrow the money and buy Coe Manufacturing Company and I want you to get on the plane and go with them to Painesville, Ohio day after tomorrow and you see to it that they've got the money to do it. The VP said yes sir and off we went. There were no questions asked, simply a handshake and it took less than an hour to accomplish.

I still see him often and I really enjoy being a friend as we've become much closer since then. I went on the Board of Directors of U.S. Bank and was on that with him for about eighteen years. That was a very enjoyable association and without John's help I would never have been able to get the start. Repayment of the five year loan was made without any question—and ahead of schedule. He and I retired from the bank board the same night when our terms expired.

JENS JORGENSEN

Jens was a hard-nosed Scandinavian who worked for Smith Wood Products in Coquille, Oregon. Smith Wood Products was built in the mid 1930s. They had a plant and a lot of good old-growth timber and experience. They sold to Coos Bay Lumber, who sold to Georgia-Pacific in 1956. Jens was the plant engineer when I first met him and he later became plant manager. Georgia-Pacific was buying several operations in the West back then, but many of the experienced people at those companies were at or nearing retiring age. Jens was a very bright guy and was still in his middle years when he became the vice president of manufacturing for Georgia-Pacific. He was a hard working guy and working for Georgia-Pacific he had to run awfully fast. He had many responsibilities, with many new plants to oversee. He was always very considerate of me even though we had our share of disagreements. When they wanted to do something he didn't hesitate to pick up the phone and call and we'd get our heads together and make some sort of a business transaction.

When G-P went South to start building southern pine plywood plants, he was in charge. He bought the veneer lathes and the dryers for the first Fordyce, Arkansas plant from us and then bought equipment from us for five more plants and another five after that and another several plants after that. In those days there were no experienced workmen. The beautiful thing for him was he had many plants in the South that had basically the same model equipment and he could move supervisors and various operators around from one plant to the other without fear of the people having trouble with inexperience. They were plants that would accommodate with ease all sorts of talent, supervisors, operators, maintenance people, electricians. It was a very simple way to get many plants on line in a very short period of time.

Home was always Coquille, Oregon for Jens, a very talented and great friend of mine. I believe Jens Jorgensen passed away in the early 1980s.

LEONARD NYSTROM

Leonard Nystrom began his career in 1921 as a laborer at the new Olympia Veneer plant in Olympia, Washington. He became superintendent of the Aberdeen Plywood operation in the 1930s in Aberdeen, Washington. The plant was a subsidiary business of Olympia Veneer. Eventually the Aberdeen plant burned down and a new mill was built in 1940 in Eugene, Oregon and Nystrom became superintendent of it. The year before that, Olympia Veneer built another plywood mill in Willamina, Oregon, called Pacific Plywood and at the beginning of the war all three mills were consolidated as Associated Plywood Mills. Right after the war they sold the original plant at Olympia, moved headquarters to Eugene and made Leonard the president. He was very instrumental in running those big mills—at least two of them had 12 ft. lathes. They were the longest in the industry. They made mostly marine grade plywood.

Leonard spoke with very broken English. He was a big man, a jovial fellow and he had many Swedes who worked with him. For some reason he always welcomed me into their offices and always gave me encouragement. As a result those little things that may have been little at the time meant so much to me later on in life. I think Leonard probably passed away in the early 1960s, so I had an association with him for a period of ten years from the early 50s to the early 60s. It was always a learning experience to be around him and his associates and sit in a meeting to discuss whatever the technological problems were. They had a group of Swedes that sat around and they could solve the most difficult problems as well as anyone. In those days there weren't very many trained engineers working in the plywood industry. They had hard-nosed Scandinavian workmen and they gained their experience the hard way and it was hard to beat them out of their ideas. If they had an idea they thought was going to work, you might try to talk them out of it, but it didn't happen very often. U.S. Plywood eventually bought Associated Plywood mills.

GENE BREWER

Gene Brewer was born on a farm in Grays Harbor County, Washington and graduated from the University of Oregon. After college he described his work as a butter-and-egg salesman. He then went to work as a junior manager for Aircraft Plywood in Seattle, which was owned by U.S. Plywood. Bill Bailey was the general manager and Gene Brewer worked for Bill for many years. U.S. Plywood and its founder Larry Ottinger had purchased Aircraft Plywood in the mid 1930s. Gene started at Aircraft around 1937 and Ottinger recognized Gene as being a bright young man. Several years later U.S. Plywood built a new hardwood plywood plant in Orangeburg, SC and when Ottinger asked Bailey to recommend someone to manage it, Bailey spoke on Gene's behalf. My first meeting with Gene was at that Orangeburg plant. We at Coe were having some machinery problems with a dryer there and I was sent to fix it. I spent a week or two there and Gene was very kind to me and we became good friends.

U.S. Plywood then bought a plant in 1949 in Anderson, California that was originally built by Harbor Plywood. Gene moved there and became the president of U.S. Plywood of California. Harbor Plywood had put in several large dry kilns, lumber kilns, to dry veneer. They were manufacturing plywood from mostly ponderosa pine logs, sugar pine and some white fir. The pine was hard to dry and it would warp badly, so Harbor Plywood thought they could dry this in kiln type drying equipment and when Brewer went there he saw what they were doing and realized they were not being successful, so he bought several dryers from Coe. I didn't sell him the dryers, but I supervised the installation of the first one and that put the plant on a profitable basis. During this period in Anderson they built a particleboard type plant called NovaPly, and Gene and Warren Smith had brought this process from Europe to Anderson and it became a very large manufacturing complex. I spent a couple of months there working for his people and for another associate named Ken Morrow, who was an industrial engineer and was Gene's assistant. Ken was put in charge of U.S. Plywood's West Coast operations when Gene became president of U.S. Plywood at the New York head office. He was president of U.S. Plywood when they merged with Champion International and he became chairman.

He left in 1970 and joined Southwest Forest Industries where he was president for several years based in Phoenix.

Gene was always on the podium at any industry event and always told everybody I was one of the first guys he had met in the industry, and that I had been associated with him all of his career. He was always a good acquaintance of mine and his wife, Helen, was a good friend of Sue, my wife. After he retired we often saw them at the Plywood Pioneers meetings and he always told the story of our having met at the plant in Orangeburg. He was one of those nice guys. He was always very eager to give me a pat on the back and that type of encouragement, which in this industry was always quite welcomed and appreciated. He became the president of the National Institute of Building Sciences in 1977 and remained in that capacity for ten years before he retired. He was very much involved in construction criteria and regulations. I was told his salary was more than the president of the United States. He died in 2004 at age 90 at his home in Newport, Oregon.

BILL HUNT

Bill Hunt was the president of Georgia-Pacific at the time when Louisiana-Pacific was spun off from G-P in 1973 and he became chairman and CEO of L-P and Harry Merlo became president. He retired in 1974 and Merlo became chairman. Bill was an athlete and played basketball and most of the other sports when he attended the University of Wisconsin at Wisconsin-Rapids, from whence he graduated. He was a school teacher and a coach then he went to work for Algoma Plywood & Veneer in Algoma, Wisconsin and became their sales manager. He went from there to work for U.S. Plywood in 1937, first in Chicago and then in New York City as the assistant to the general sales manager, and then was a branch manager for U.S. Plywood in Cleveland. Then he was an assistant general manager back at the Algoma plant, which U.S. Plywood bought, and he became manager for U.S. Plywood in Detroit, and then back to Chicago as

Midwest Division manager. He moved back to New York City as vice president in charge of sales.

He was a big, tall guy, 6-foot-7 or so, and he was very popular and knew everyone in the athletic world. He was hearty guy and really a first class salesman. In 1957 Georgia-Pacific hired him away from U.S. Plywood as G-P's vice president for plywood and specialty sales based in Portland. He continued to do an excellent job and Georgia-Pacific was a growing company and eventually he was brought along as an executive vice president for building products, and in 1970 he became president of Georgia-Pacific. He also served as president of American Plywood Association. He and I met way back when he was with U.S. Plywood in New York and when he moved to Portland I grew to know him well. When Jens Jorgensen was given the assignment at G-P of buying machinery for those southern pine plywood plants, Jens told Bill he wanted to buy the machinery from Coe and Bill said that's just fine, I know Fred. When I went to see Jens at G-P's office without my knowing the reason for his calling, Bill and Jens got off the elevator and we talked a few minutes and Bill told me Jens had some things he wanted to talk to me about and you guys go down the hall and get to work. He was obviously very instrumental in my being able to successfully sell Georgia-Pacific their machinery for all of those plants. Those were the most productive days in the selling of plywood machinery that Coe had ever known. We sold G-P the machinery for seventeen plants and Bill was very much a part of it.

HAROLD ERICKSON

Harold was a very bright engineer but unfortunately he had an illness and he stayed very thin. He was a native of North Dakota and graduated from the University of Washington. He worked for an engineering company in Tacoma called Industrial Development Company and they did specialized design work for the construction of various types of manufacturing plants and he also worked as a design engineer with the Plywood Research

Foundation for several years; so he had a broad range of experiences before going to work for Weyerhaeuser in 1958. He was very innovative and he was always involved in the design of machinery or plants and he had a staff of engineers who worked for him. He was an individual that you could make book on his intelligence and if he said something you either accepted it—and I'm not saying he was heavy handed—or you needed to find some reason to not believe it. In other words he had done his homework very well and he was right I'd say eighty percent of the time. He was not right one-hundred percent of the time, but I would bet on him one-hundred percent of the time. He had numerous patents in his name involving veneer production and drying as well as composite board manufacturing.

I really enjoyed working with him and I learned a great deal from him. I had a great appreciation for the intellect that he had and many other people felt the same way about him. I know George Weyerhaeuser felt the same way about him. When Harold was with Weyerhaeuser, the wood products division had 1,100 engineers in their research and development department and he was one of top four or five key guys. Very well liked. You have a tendency to get along and associate with people that you like and we had developed a good friendship over a long period of time. I usually dealt with Weyerhaeuser's engineering department and Harold Erickson was the guy I always felt was the really smart guy in the group, not that there weren't a lot of other smart guys, but he was the guy who could think through deep problems and I had fun trying to match wits with guys like that. He always had fresh ideas. He held different titles at Weyerhaeuser through the years—from engineer to facilities planning manager to manager of research and development. He died young in September 1973 at age 50.

GENE KNOKEY

Gene Knokey came with us in 1967 while he was a manager of Edward Hines Lumber Company's plant at Burns, Oregon.

He had grown up on the West Coast and Burns is way over in the high desert part of Oregon and I think he was anxious to move back to the rain forest areas. He and his father had always worked in plywood plants, for Associated Plywood Mills, Anacortes Veneer in Anacortes, Washington; Columbia Veneer, Kalama, Washington; and he had worked as a manger for a lumber and plywood plant for Diamond Lumber Company at Tillamook, Oregon also before Edward Hines. So he had the experience of manufacturing and supervising large crews, 500 to 600 people, and their manufacturing operations. His father was a master mechanic in several plants and Gene had grown up working with his father so he had a lot of good experience and background for someone in the machinery business. He knew everybody in the industry, knew every plant and every manager, and had a good reputation. Very jovial fellow and generally a good guy. He was smart, had good ideas and he and his father had done some innovative engineering work that developed certain types of machinery when they were operating plants together.

Gene had the type of experience that fit into Coe's business hand to glove. He became my assistant and was vice president of our Western Operations until he retired. He was needed as part of the progress of moving into the South and the southern pine plywood business. He became very much involved in that. He had meaningful associations with people at Weyerhaeuser so when they went South and started building plywood plants Gene was very much involved. He was also very involved with Boise Cascade projects in the South, Hunt Lumber in Louisiana and several others.

Gene retired before I sold the company. He was a little bit like myself, a workaholic, and his wife became somewhat disenchanted about his working too much and too hard. They were originally from Anacortes and they moved back to Anacortes after he retired. He and his dad built several boats in excess of fifty feet in length, big motor vessels, and they loved to fish and they loved the water.

ART MCGEE

In 1973, several years before I bought Coe Company when I was vice president in the West, I needed a chief engineer as we were growing quickly. We eventually hired Art McGee then working for FMC, the old Food Machinery Corporation, in San Jose, California. Art was a very well educated, very smart guy. He was running their research and development department and he had gone to school at Stanford and received his master's degree from the University of California at Berkeley and had both mechanical engineering and electrical engineering degrees. It was in those days that computers were just beginning to enter our industry. They had been around for a number of years in accounting, but in the manufacture of lumber and plywood, computers were not generally known until the late 60s and early 70s. Art bought that level of expertise with him. He turned out to be an exceptional engineer and he was always interested in developing software to control computers. He helped us buy the Nosler laser scanner business as we needed the measuring devices with which to use computers and to program that type of equipment.

Art was involved in I suppose twenty different patents that we had; some were joint patents with Gene Knokey and others in the engineering department. In some cases he was probably more involved in the ideas in the patents than showed up on the patents themselves as we liked to give some of the younger people credit for being innovative and we oftentimes put other people's names on patents even though someone else was the innovator. Art stayed with the company his entire career and retired in 1996. Art was a quiet but exceptional person who was liked and respected by all who knew him.

CHAPTER TWENTY-TWO

CURTAIN CALL

Somebody asked me what I could attribute my success to. I didn't take long to answer. Hard work. Hard work. Hard work. Hard work develops experience and experience is very important. You must be willing to apply yourself and work many hours a day to become acquainted with not only your machinery but the employees you have that are involved and the customers you deal with, knowing as much about their business as you know about your own business or more.

In that regard, I was fortunate to have been raised in an environment of having to work hard. Back on our farm in Alexandria, Indiana, hard work was a no brainer. When I was ten and became old enough to help my brother with the farming, the depression was still lingering. Nobody could afford to slack off, or else the entire family could suffer. So no matter what other interests you had, what other jobs you had, what sports you played, what girls you liked, that all came in a distant second to the chores on the farm.

I still go back and visit Alexandria now and then. My brother Don and various nieces and nephews still live in the area. When I go back I pass by those one-hundred acres that I had my nose in every day. There was someone living on that land until about fifteen years ago. Our old farmhouse and the barns and the orchard and the gardens have all been turned over into farmland now. Some years ago my nephew, who was farming the farm at the time, tore down the house. I don't know how old it was. I know my dad bought the farm and the house in 1927. The underpinning consisted of hand hewn timbers but decay had gotten into them and it wasn't structurally sound.

We didn't sell the farmland until a few years ago. When my mother died she had left it to my sister, Marienne. When Marienne died I had a plan to pass it along to the nephews and nieces but nobody wanted it. Some years ago I had purchased about 350 acres of cultivated land in the area and I offered that as well. I was going to help them to get it financed and organized for them to share ownership, about nineteen of them, but the ones who were still in farming didn't think they could do it. So I sold it and split up the proceeds between all of them.

Of course the older we get, the more immediate family members we lose along the way, and today only my brother Don, along with myself, is still living. Don lives nears Indianapolis and stays busy helping people who are incapacitated and who can't hold a full time job. He took care of my sister, Marienne, the last few years of her life. Before the war Don farmed my grandmother's farm and then he served as a Merchant Marine during the war. After getting out he worked for the Allison Jet Engine Division of General Motors in their research and development department and made his career there.

Among my siblings who have died: My oldest brother Everett at one time worked in the automobile industry for General Motors and then got into the restaurant business, buying one with his wife in Muncie, Indiana and operating it all through their three children's upbringings.

The second oldest child, Louise, was the first in the family to go to college, Anderson College business school, and upon finishing there she went to work for Container Corporation. She was promoted and she went to their headquarters in Cincinnati. When she moved, my sister Marienne also moved to Cincinnati, and Louise took care of her. Louise never married as she was always looking after Marienne. Marienne, as I've stated elsewhere in this book, despite her handicap, became a champion of incapacitated individuals and was recognized in Cincinnati as a Woman of the Year.

My second oldest brother, Bob, always worked for General Motors or Chrysler and eventually retired from Chrysler Corporation in Kokomo, Indiana. The third brother, Eugene, as I've stated, served in the 82nd Airborne and was seriously wounded in Europe, but survived to live a normal life. He was in the wholesale petroleum business and various other businesses. My younger sister, Betty Jean, married and moved to Tampa, Florida. She passed away within the past couple of years.

So what does an old-timer like myself do in the twilight of his life, besides go back and visit the farm. One thing he does is spend a lot of time with his wife of fifty plus years, and one thing they both do is give financial resources to worthy projects. When I was working all the time and traveling I didn't contribute much to such endeavors because I didn't have time to understand what I might be donating to. But now we have the time and wherewithal to do so and are very happy to do that, especially for colleges such as Lewis & Clark College in Portland, Lake Erie College in Painesville and the University of Portland. I was on the board of trustees at Lewis & Clark College for nineteen years and was chairman for three years. I spent quite a bit of time at that after selling Coe. I provided some considerable funding for a new Visual Arts building, which they graciously named the Fred W. Fields Center for the Visual Arts. My wife and I made a significant donation to the University of Portland in 2008 toward the construction of two new student residence halls. We made the donation in honor of her brother, the

Rev. Arthur Schoenfeldt, who was a university priest and who had died the previous year. The school named them the Rev. Arthur Schoenfeldt, C.S.C. Hall and the Fred and Suzanne Fields Hall. Meanwhile I'm on the board of the Columbia River Maritime Museum, and am now going back on the board of the Portland Art Museum. I was on the board of the Oregon Museum of Science and Industry and have been on the board of World Forestry Center for a long time. Sue has long served on the University of Portland's Board of Regents, and she has been a board member for the Portland Art Museum, Oregon Humane Society and the Boys and Girls Aid Society. I mention these things to show that there is life in retirement.

I also have some land and recently sold land on which the community of Tigard built a new library. I am currently developing some timberland that I acquired years ago near Coe's plant in Tigard.

One project I have been involved in is the development of the AMES machine. That stands for Assisted Movement with Enhanced Sensation. It's a device to improve the ability of stroke patients to regain some of their capabilities in their affected limbs. My involvement stems from a stroke I sustained in 2001.

I had gone into the hospital and had a knee replacement procedure one morning, about 10 a.m. About 4 p.m. that afternoon I started to regain my senses after being heavily sedated and asleep, and I realized I couldn't move my right side. I could feel it in my eyelid, my mouth, my entire right side. It was a devastating experience I can assure you. Fortunately I was able to push the emergency button beside the bed on my left side for help. The nurses were in there in a matter of seconds. So the stroke was caught within a couple of hours after it occurred. We started with the rehab program the next day, and it took me four or five months to get back to using all of my facilities. For a while I rehabbed with a prototype AMES machine, but it really wasn't for someone like me, because as the doctors said my stroke had been tended to very quickly and I was able to gain back my facilities on my right side so quickly. But this device interested me and it seemed to have a lot of potential.

The inventor of this procedure is Dr. Paul Cordo. He invented it while working at the Oregon Health & Science University in Portland. The patents are in the name of the University and they've been assigned to Dr. Cordo and the company he has formed, AMES Technology. Dr. Cordo is the former director of the Neurological Sciences Institute at the university. I participate in the company as a board member and I've contributed considerable money to the building of test devices and tests on patients.

It's a device where a person sits down in a chair or a wheelchair and his or her limb is strapped into an electro mechanical and computerized device. For example, a patient's hand may be strapped in this device; the device will open and close the hand even though the person can't maneuver the hand. There's a vibrator on the back of the wrist and when the hand is opening, the vibrator is vibrating at a very high rate of speed. It stimulates the nerve signal to the brain. When closing the hand there's a vibrator that vibrates on the inside of the wrist and again that stimulates the nerve signal going back to the brain. When a normal, healthy person wants to close his hand the first thing that has to happen is that a message has to be sent to the brain and the brain sends a message back. In a stroke patient the brain cells in that part of the brain have become deadened, so you're trying to reactive the cells adjacent the dead cells and that is possible by the certain maneuvers with the muscles and nerves in the hand. Going through these exercises and as time goes on one gains strength as the machine is computerized to where it increases the amount of strength that is required by the hand to perform these functions. What's happening is you're increasing the amount of strength in that hand or any affected limb which in turn is activating the brain cells adjacent the dead brain cells and this can eventually improve the person's capability. As the name suggests, it's based on the hypothesis that assisted movement and enhanced sensation, used together, promotes the functional reorganization of sensorimotor pathways in the brain. This will help a lot of people, but there are some people where more brain cells are dead than can be reactivated.

We built ten of these machines in Portland at a cost of about $100,000 each. The ten machines have been installed in hospitals throughout the country, one in Atlanta, two in Chicago, one in Spokane, one in Seattle, one in San Francisco, one in Portland and elsewhere. They can't be sold or put into production until they've gone through a clinical test by the Food and Drug Administration. We are compelled to test at least 160 different patient limbs. We have to perform these tests with the device and at the same time we simulate these same functions on 160 other limbs of patients who don't know that they aren't being treated with the use of the device, but you have to be able to compare the results of the one being tested with the device and the one being simulated. We expect to have these tests completed in early 2010.

During these tests we're not informed as to the results, successful or not. The test results have to be examined by a committee or a board who read the results and make the determination as to whether the equipment is successful. We don't know until we complete the entire testing program as to the success or failure of the apparatus. So it's a long expensive process with a lot of uncertainty until the end. We're getting favorable vibes and we can talk to the patients, and sometimes it seems as though we're performing miracles and other times it seems as though we're pounding sand. There are other investors besides myself. The University is an investor and Dr. Cordo, and we have a president of the company, Roger Wyle. We don't have a big staff. Dr. Cordo's wife is a nurse and she oversees the test procedures. Dr. Cordo prepares the instructions for the installation and the procedures the technicians use in the field. It isn't easy to find resources to do these things. We applied for a government grant and we've been notified we're going to receive a grant of a million dollars from the National Health Sciences Institute in Washington. That will go a long way. It's rather interesting, sometimes discouraging, but most everything you do in life has its ups and downs.

So I stay active in many ways really, including my membership in the Committee of 25. This is a group of past executives who meet once a week during the winter months in Palm Springs, California. We call it the Committee of 25 but we have probably 100 members. George Weyerhaeuser is a member, so is Bill Boeing, Jr., son of the founder of Boeing Aircraft. Tom Moore, the former president of ABC Television, was a member until he passed away a couple of years ago. We invite speakers of various descriptions to talk about the economy, medical issues or water supply in southern California, subjects which are interesting to people such as myself who have been in business most all of their lives. My wife and I have a place at Indian Wells, near Palm Springs. We also have a place at Gearhart on the Oregon coast, in addition to our home in the West Hills neighborhood in Portland. We bounce around between them as the seasons change.

It's not all fun and games as the older you get the more you deal with issues of your health. In the summer of 2008 I had two blockages of arteries in my lower legs and had those rotor-rootered as I call it. They usually operate in the morning and release the patient the same afternoon. But they kept me overnight. While I was in the hospital bed that night, my heart stopped for several seconds. They had me wired and the nurses caught it and got everything back in sync very quickly. I didn't know this had happened. I was only aware that some nurses had come in during the night and seemed to be doing something to the monitors and wires and then left the room.

The next morning my doctor and another doctor came in and told me my heart had stopped that night. I said "oh really?" He said you need a pacemaker and this is Dr. Feldman and he's going to give you one. I said when do we do that, and he said now. I said what does "now" mean. He said Mr. Fields your bed is on wheels and you're going to the operating room "now." I received a pacemaker and everything has performed very well since. As for when my heart was stopped, I don't recall seeing the Pearly Gates or a White Light or anybody with a pitchfork.